WITH ALL MY
MIND

God's Design for Mental Wellness

by James P. Porowski

LifeWay Press
Nashville, Tennessee

ISBN 0-6330-0584-3

This book is a resource in the Personal Life category of the Christian Growth Study Plan.
Course CG-0536

Dewey Decimal Classification: 153
Subject Heading: MENTAL HEALTH

Branda Polk, Health Ministry Specialist
Betty Hassler, Editor-in-Chief
Jon Rodda, Art Director
Jimmy Abegg, Illustrator
Joyce McGregor, Editor
Beth Shive, Copy Editor

To order additional copies of this resource: WRITE LifeWay Church Resources Customer Service; One LifeWay Plaza; Nashville, TN 37234-0113; FAX order to (615) 251-5933; PHONE (800) 458-2772; EMAIL to *customerservice@lifeway.com*; ORDER ONLINE at *www.lifeway.com*; or VISIT the LifeWay Christian Store serving you.

Printed in the United States of America

☩

Adult Ministry Publishing
LifeWay Church Resources
One LifeWay Plaza
Nashville, TN 37234-0175

Table of Contents

AN INTRODUCTION TO *Fit4*

With All My Mind: God's Design for Mental Wellness is one of four continuing studies in *Fit 4: A LifeWay Christian Wellness Plan.* If this is your first *Fit 4* study, welcome to this series which helps individuals achieve wellness one wise choice at a time. Wellness is a lifestyle which includes all four areas of our lives: emotional, spiritual, mental, and physical.

Although this study emphasizes mental wellness, the other areas of wellness are referred to throughout the book because whole-person health involves all that we are. Jesus said it best in Mark 12:30-31—the *Fit 4* theme verses—when He outlined a wellness lifestyle: " 'Love the Lord your God with all your heart and with all your soul and with all your mind and with all your strength. Love your neighbor as yourself.' "

Fit 4 emphasizes three Lifestyle Disciplines to help you live a balanced lifestyle. **UPREACH** is your relationship to God through daily prayer, Bible reading, and listening to God. **OUTREACH** is your relationship with others. **INREACH** is caring for yourself mentally, emotionally, physically, and spiritually. Each week of this study you will find information in the margins which will give you practical suggestions for implementing each of these disciplines daily.

Since our emotions are housed in a body which requires proper food and nutrition to function properly, you will also find in each week a helpful suggestion from our friend Professor Phitt, one of the hosts in the *Fit 4* videos that accompany the two basic courses. These suggestions, found in the margin of each week's reading, will guide you as you make wise choices in exercise and nutrition.

Your *Accountability Journal* will be your friend on your wellness journey. On pages 6-10 you will find information on how to use the *Journal* to track your exercise and food choices for the next 12 weeks. Record your exercise to see patterns, make changes, and set goals to improve your fitness level. Record the food you eat so you become aware of the types and amounts of your daily choices. For more information on making these wise choices, consult pages 14-22 of your *Journal.*

Your group will support your wellness journey. While you encourage and support others, they will do the same for you. Your facilitator will also encourage you as you journey toward mental wellness. Plan to be present for each group session. Contribute your ideas, ask questions, and seek answers from other group members' struggles, victories, and life experiences.

For additional information on a wellness lifestyle, consider being part of a *Fit 4* basic course. *Fit 4 Nutrition* is a 12-week course that will help you apply the *Fit 4* Guidelines for Healthy Eating. *Fit 4 Fitness* is a 12-week course that will help you develop your own personalized fitness plan.

You will also want to participate in the other three continuing studies: *Fit 4 With All My Heart: God's Design for Emotional Wellness,* 0-6330-0583-5; *Fit 4 With All My Soul: God's Design for Spiritual Wellness,* 0-6330-0585-1; and *Fit 4 With All My Strength: God's Design for Physical Wellness,* 0-6330-0586-X. Information about ordering these and other *Fit 4* resources is found on page 95.

ABOUT THE AUTHOR

Dr. James P. Porowski is a professor of child and family development at Southeastern Baptist Theological Seminary and the Director of Family Life Resources, a counseling center in Raleigh, North Carolina. James co-authored *Strength for the Journey: A Biblical Perspective on Discouragement and Depression* (LifeWay Press, 1999).

James is a licensed psychologist with a doctorate in clinical psychology from George Fox University. He received his Th.M. from Dallas Theological Seminary and his B.A. from Texas Christian University. He and his wife Ginny have four children, Stephanie, Jody, Corinne, and Bridget. James is also a certified sports psychologist and enjoys running, writing, and spending time with Ginny and their four daughters.

ABOUT THE STUDY

With All My Mind: God's Design for Mental Wellness is intended as a group study over a 12-week period. The first week's group session will give you an overview of *Fit 4: A LifeWay Christian Wellness Plan*. During this session, you will complete the video viewer guide on page 6.

During the following 10 weeks, you will read each week's content and complete the learning activities which are marked with the *Fit 4* logo ( ). Read the week's material at your own pace. Make sure you complete the reading before the weekly group session. The learning activities provide practice and review for the concepts you will learn. They also improve retention of what you read. A Verse to Know at the beginning of each week will enable you to commit to memory specific verses which will aid you in your wellness journey.

In the margins you will read suggestions for implementing the three Lifestyle Disciplines of *Fit 4:* UPREACH, OUTREACH, INREACH. You will also find helpful advice from our friend Professor Phitt, one of the video hosts from the *Fit 4* basic courses. Professor Phitt will give suggestions for exercise and nutrition choices. The *Accountability Journal* accompanying this book will also encourage you in your wellness journey.

A Leader Guide on pages 88-94 provides the group facilitator with specific information for beginning and conducting a class using *With All My Mind*. Week 12 of this study is a group session which provides an opportunity for members to evaluate progress toward goals, set new goals for maintaining a wellness lifestyle, and make plans for participating in other *Fit 4* or discipleship studies.

Remember our *Fit 4* motto: Wellness is achieved one wise choice at a time.

Introduction
VIEWER GUIDE

1. *Fit 4* is designed to help you develop a _____ approach to wellness.

2. What is wellness?

3. The secret to good health is _____.

4. You will use the *Fit 4* guidelines to develop a _____ plan to meet your needs.

5. What is the purpose of your *Fit 4* group?

6. What is the role of your *Fit 4* facilitator?

7. Who is Professor Phitt?

8. Why is seeking wellness important to your relationship with God?

9. What are the Lifestyle Disciplines of *Fit 4?* U_____, O_____, and I_____.

10. Based on what you know thus far, list some personal benefits you can expect to gain from completing this study.

Welcome to this course in the continuing studies series of *Fit 4*. This may be your first experience with *Fit 4* and that's OK. Each of the continuing studies highlights one of the four areas of wellness from Mark 12:30. We want to grow in loving the Lord our God with all our hearts, souls, minds, and strength. We want to remind ourselves continually that we cannot compartmentalize our lives. Each of the four areas affects the others, and when we recognize this truth, we are better equipped to live a healthy, balanced lifestyle.

In each week's study you will find in the margins of the text several ideas to help you grow in the three disciplines of *Fit 4:* UPREACH, OUTREACH, and INREACH. UPREACH activities help you strengthen your personal relationship with God. Certainly the God who created the universe deserves to be loved totally. Read Jesus' words—this week's Verses to Know—in the margin.

When Jesus gave the command to love God, He also told us to love our neighbors as we love ourselves. To help you accomplish this important task, OUTREACH activities encourage improved relationships with others. INREACH activities help you care for yourself because you are to love others as you love yourself. Also in the margins you will find ideas from Professor Phitt, a character from the *Fit 4* videos for the basic Nutrition and Fitness courses. He will give you ideas for better nutrition and fitness. Complete the margin activities each week.

THE ACCOUNTABILITY JOURNAL

If you've completed the Nutrition and Fitness studies in *Fit 4*, continue to use your *Accountability Journal* to stay on your wellness journey. If this is the first *Fit 4* study you've taken, you will find basic information about nutrition and fitness in the *Accountability Journal* that accompanies this workbook. Begin by reading "Introduction to This Journal" and "How to Use This Journal" on pages 6 and 7. Locate the sample page detailing how to fill out the daily journal on page 10.

The *Fit 4* plan reminds us that Jesus did not say, *love God with all your mind and neglect the rest.* God always deals with the whole person that He created. You can't

VERSES TO KNOW

" 'Love the Lord your God with all your heart and with all your soul and with all your mind and with all your strength.' The second is this: 'Love your neighbor as yourself.' "
—Mark 12:30-31

be totally healthy in mind and remain unhealthy in spirit, emotions, and physical strength. That's why we encourage you to practice the disciplines of *Fit 4* during this 12-week study. *Discipline* may sound like an unwelcome word, but fortunately discipline is transferable; when we become disciplined in one area of life, we discover it becomes easier to be disciplined in other areas.

GOALS FOR OUR STUDY

In this first week we want to lay a foundation for this study. The goal will be to learn what it means to love God with all of our minds. We will carefully consider what the Bible means by the word *mind*.

Our Scripture for the study will primarily come from the letters of the apostle Paul and what has been communicated about him in the Book of Acts. No one in the New Testament discussed the concept of the mind more than Paul. For him it was a central issue for successful Christian living. Over the next few weeks you will find that his writings on the subject will encourage you as you learn how to control and direct your thoughts in a positive, upward way. You will look at some of the obstacles all of us face as we seek to love God with all our minds, as well as the steps found in the Bible for transforming our thoughts.

Our goal is mental wellness, so we will be exploring what marks an individual as mentally healthy. The apostle Paul had a goal for those he loved and worked with; he desired for them to be complete, or mature in Christ (Col. 1:28). We will be working together during the course of this study to grasp what this goal means for our lives. We will be most concerned with studying the mind but will be careful to center it within the foremost commandment of Christ to " 'Love the Lord your God with all your heart and with all your soul and with all your mind and with all your strength' " (Mark 12:30).

Professor Phitt says:
Goal-setting is an important part of the *Fit 4 Wellness Plan*. Read pages 14-23 of your *Accountability Journal* for information on how to set healthy eating and exercise goals for the next 10 weeks.

As you begin, what are your personal goals for this study? List them.

_____

_____

_____

THE APOSTLE PAUL AND MENTAL WELLNESS

My choice to use the writings of Paul to provide focus and continuity for our study grows out of his unique God-given mission to teach the church. He was a man of remarkable learning who bridged the gap between Jewish and Gentile thinking. Paul would quickly point to his Lord, Jesus Christ, as the center of his life: "I consider everything a loss compared to the surpassing greatness of knowing Christ Jesus my Lord" (Phil. 3:8).

The great church historian, Philip Schaff, described Paul as "the most remarkable and influential character in history."[1] Paul was born a Roman citizen. He was able to pass freely throughout the Roman world. He was educated in Jerusalem under the famous rabbi Gamaliel and understood the Old Testament better than most Jews of his day. Paul was also fluent in Greek literature and thought. He confidently discussed the truth of Jesus Christ with anyone. With this great breadth of education, he was a teacher "of three worlds: Jewish, Greek, and Roman."[2]

Read Acts 11:19-26 in your Bible. Shortly after a new church was born in Antioch, the believers in Jerusalem sent Barnabas to encourage them. When he arrived and saw large numbers being brought to the Lord, he left to find Paul. Barnabas was humble enough to know that these disciples needed a strong teacher. Paul taught for an entire year, and here the disciples were first called Christians.

Later in Paul's ministry, when he made his defense before the governor Festus and King Agrippa, Festus revealed that the great learning of Paul was widely known. When Paul began talking about the resurrection of Christ, Festus declared with astonishment, " 'You are out of your mind, Paul! ... Your great learning is driving you insane.' "To this Paul quickly responded and set the matter straight, " 'I am not insane, most excellent Festus' " (Acts 26:24-25).

Don't get too concerned at this point. Most of us will never be driven insane by our great learning! But hopefully we will be able to grasp a better understanding of the key place that our minds and thought processes play in our daily Christian lives. Each chapter of this study begins with a prominent verse from one of Paul's letters. Seek to develop and apply to your own life the insights you gain.

THE MIND INFLUENCES THE WHOLE PERSON

We can't separate our thoughts from our feelings or spirituality, nor can we separate our minds from our bodies. Everything about us is interconnected—the reason why we use the term *wholeness* in **Fit 4**. When we direct every aspect of our lives to God—heart, soul, mind, and strength—He is the One who holds the different components in balance.

Your Mind Influences Your Heart

King David demonstrated the close connection between the mind and the heart. He prayed in Psalm 139:23, "Search me, O God, and know my heart; test me and know my anxious thoughts." In Hebrew poetry one line is often followed by another line with similar ideas. When they are taken together, they make a statement that carries greater force. Here David said that he wanted God to search and test him. He linked his heart with his anxious thoughts.

 If you prayed for God to search your heart, what emotions would He discover? Circle all the ones that apply.

love   fear   joy   anxiety   peace   shame

anger   confusion   sadness   relief   guilt

INREACH
As you read this section, give an example of how your thoughts affect your

emotions _____

_____

spirit _____

_____

body _____

_____

David went on to ask God to "See if there is any offensive way in me, and lead me in the way everlasting" (Ps. 139:24). He wanted God to know both his thoughts and his feelings, and to help him live as he should. In this study we will see that at times our thoughts will generate certain emotions, and at other times our emotions will shade our thinking in one direction or another. If you have not done so, I hope you will one day complete the *Fit 4* study *With All My Heart: God's Design for Emotional Wellness* to explore more of the emotional component of loving God. [3] Your mind influences your heart, but it also has an effect on your spirit.

Your Mind Influences Your Spirit

There is no such thing as neutral thinking. Thoughts are always directed toward something. [4] We generally have our minds set on something or someone. This truth will be one of the central concerns of the apostle Paul in this study. In fact, we read in Romans 8:5, "Those who live according to the sinful nature have their minds set on what that nature desires; but those who live in accordance with the Spirit have their minds set on what the Spirit desires."

Paul was telling us that we can make a choice about how to "set" or direct our thoughts. Our minds certainly have a real influence on our spirits. We will take a longer look at this important topic in the next few weeks. If you have not worked through the *Fit 4* study *With All My Soul: God's Design for Spiritual Wellness,* I hope you will examine God's design for spiritual wellness in more detail. [5]

A. W. Tozer vividly demonstrates the relationship between the mind and the spirit in his book *The Knowledge of the Holy.* "Were we able to extract from any man a complete answer to the question, 'What comes into your mind when you think about God?' we might predict with certainty the spiritual future of that man." [6]

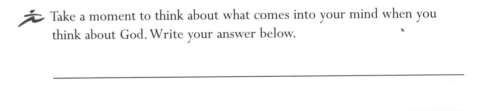 Take a moment to think about what comes into your mind when you think about God. Write your answer below.

_____

_____

If you view God as a harsh judge, you will probably have a negative attitude toward developing a closer relationship with Him. If you view God as a loving Father, you will no doubt have a stronger desire for a close relationship with Him.

Your Mind Influences Your Body

Think about a time when you were in a dark place and someone came up behind you and said, "Boo!" Can you remember how your body felt? Suddenly electrified and ready to strike your former friend? Perhaps you were ready to run away as fast as possible! This reaction is what scientists call the fight or flight response. God has designed our bodies so that when we perceive a threat (we think about it), we are energized to confront it or get out of the way fast.

UPREACH

What do you have your mind set on? Evaluate your thoughts over the next few days. Are they mainly about you, your activities, and your plans? What place does God occupy in your thought life?

last   middle   first

A lie detector test works this way. When a person is asked various questions, immediate reactions in the body can be measured. If a person responds with the truth, heart beat, perspiration, and body tension remain steady. However, if the average person lies, his or her heart beat increases, perspiration rises, and the body becomes more tense.

On page 12 you will see The Stress Model diagram. The diagram, found in all of the *Fit 4* continuing studies, illustrates the interrelation between the emotional, mental, and physical parts of a person. On the chart you can identify the mental function with beliefs, attitudes, and thoughts. You can also locate the emotional component. The diagram shows how the events we experience, filtered through our beliefs and attitudes, lead to thoughts and emotions.

 Examine The Stress Model diagram to understand the basic concepts it pictures. Then answer the question in your own words: Where on the diagram do you locate the mind?

Beliefs, attitudes, and thoughts are all mental processes. Pay special attention to the last bold-lettered statement on page 12: Because we each have the ability to change our thoughts, we can change how we feel. God made us with the capacity to change. God is the Creator. Scientists do not create; they simply discover what God has done (if their research has been carried out in an objective manner). You will find that as we explore mental wellness together, negative moods and attitudes can be transformed as we learn to change our thinking. In weeks 8 and 9 we will focus on the important process of being transformed by the renewing of our minds. Read Romans 12:2 in the margin.

> Because we each have the ability to change our thoughts, we can change how we feel.

 Using ideas from The Stress Model diagram, consider the following stressful event and the types of thoughts and emotions it may produce in an individual's life.

Event	Thoughts	Emotions
Flat tire	There goes my whole day!	anxiety, frustration
	-OR-	
Flat tire	This is a small problem, but with God's help I'll get through it.	less anxiety, more calm

Now you try one. Read the instructions on page 13, following the Stress Model.

> Do not conform any longer to the pattern of this world, but be transformed by the renewing of your mind. Then you will be able to test and approve what God's will is—his good, pleasing and perfect will.
> —Romans 12:2

THE STRESS MODEL

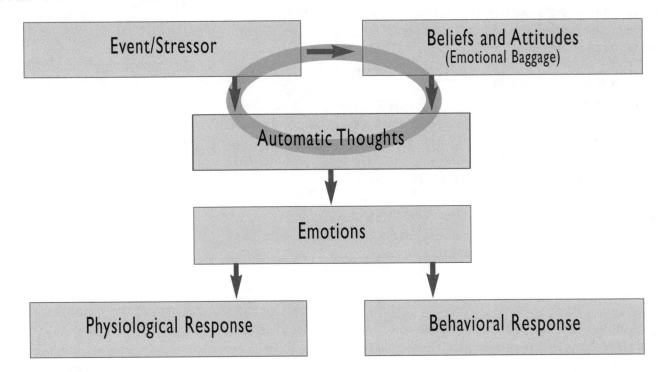

This diagram, adapted from one used at the Mind/Body Medical Institute at Harvard*, shows us how stress works its way into our lives. As **events** come into our awareness, they may or may not become **stressors**. Whether they become stressors depends on the interaction between the event and our personal history, something we can think of as our **beliefs and attitudes** or simply as "emotional baggage." Everyone has baggage! Each individual's baggage is the sum total of the beliefs and attitudes developed in response to past events in his or her life. Some baggage is useful—if you put your hand on a hot stove, it will burn you. Some no longer serve a purpose—if I cross the street without holding someone's hand, I may be hit by a car. Often we continue to hold onto emotional baggage even after it no longer serves us.

Events that take place interact with our beliefs and attitudes and lead to **automatic thoughts**—the unconscious thoughts we have all day long. The majority of our thoughts tend to be negative simply because they try to help us prepare for whatever might happen to us. They

also open us to potentially distorted thoughts. Thoughts lead to **emotions**. Emotions are biochemical and physiological as well as mental. These biochemical changes can lead to **physiological** changes that we call stress. They also produce **behavioral** responses.

Notice that **thoughts precede emotions** and that emotions are biochemical changes in your body. This process sets up a cycle or loop in which your mind identifies the biochemical events and labels them as an emotion. Certain biochemical changes may be identified as anger, sadness, happiness, or joy—but the point is that thought precedes emotions. Think happy thoughts, experience happy emotions. Think angry thoughts, feel anger.

Because we each have the ability to change our thoughts, we can change how we feel. We are not helpless victims of our emotions. We have power that we can choose to exercise. Abraham Lincoln has been quoted as saying, "Most people are about as happy as they make up their minds to be." He was right.

* Adapted from Herbert Benson, M.D., and Eileen Stuart, R.N.C., M.S., *The Wellness Book: The Comprehensive Guide to Maintaining Health and Treating Stress-Related Illness* (New York: Simon & Schuster, 1993).

List a recent stressful event. Think back to the thoughts and emotions you experienced. Record them as accurately and as objectively as possible.

Event	Thoughts	Emotions
_____	_____	_____
_____	_____	_____
_____	_____	_____

A GUIDE TO MENTAL WELLNESS

In this study you will discover how you can actually change your reactions to different events in your life by changing the way you think about them. You will see why God wanted Paul to convey to believers in the early church certain ideas about how the mind works and how these truths are every bit as important for us today as they were for the first believers.

In this study, I have chosen to describe mentally well persons as those who have a growing relationship with God, a healthy view of themselves, and a genuine love and concern for others. Consider these three aspects as you read the list below. We will be weaving in elements of each of these throughout the course of this study.

1. Mentally well persons have a growing relationship with God.
   • They love God and have an upward focus.
   • They have a biblical worldview.
   • They seek to be transformed by the renewing of their minds.
   • They practice spiritual disciplines such as Bible study, prayer, fellowship, and sharing their faith with others.
   • They seek godly wisdom and are learning and growing.

2. They have a healthy view of themselves.
   • They regard their unique personality as a gift from God.
   • They have a healthy view of self and the body God has given them.
   • They understand the danger of temptations and deceptions.
   • They are not burdened by unrealistic thinking such as perfectionism, all or nothing thinking, or self-condemnation.
   • They understand how emotional problems such as depression and anxiety can affect thinking.
   • They are able to manage stress.

3. They have a genuine love and concern for others.
   • They have a humble estimation of themselves.
   • They are focused on others and not themselves.
   • They have relationships that provide encouragement and support.

OUTREACH

As you study mental wellness over the next 10 weeks, think about how your thought processes affect others in your circle of influence—family, friends, coworkers, and neighbors.

You will have an opportunity to evaluate your mental wellness in each of these three areas. Remember that to some degree you are guessing the meanings implied by some of these statements. They will become clearer to you as we study each area. In addition, you may not have as much self-awareness now as you will have at the conclusion of this study.

Do the best you can to give an honest evaluation. Evaluating yourself more positively than accurately will help no one, especially you. You will not be asked to share this evaluation with your group. Later in the study, you will have opportunity to complete this evaluation again as a way to measure your progress over the next 10 weeks.

 Which of the following areas of mental wellness are areas of strength or weakness for you? Take a moment to reflect on your life and evaluate yourself on the scale provided by placing an X at the appropriate spot.

A growing relationship with God

Weakness   Strength

A healthy view of myself

Weakness   Strength

A genuine love and concern for others

Weakness   Strength

[1]Philip Schaff, *History of the Christian Church* (Grand Rapids: Wm. B. Eerdmans Publishing Company, 1985), 286.
[2]Bruce L. Shelley, *Church History in Plain Language* (Waco: Word Books, 1982), 33.
[3]Paul Carlisle, *With All My Heart: God's Design for Emotional Wellness* (Nashville: LifeWay Press, 2000)
[4]J. Goetzmann, "Mind," *The New International Dictionary Of New Testament Theology,* vol.2, ed. Colin Brown (Grand Rapids: Zondervan Publishing House, 1986), 617.
[5]Gene Wilkes, *With All My Soul: God's Design for Spiritual Wellness* (Nashville: LifeWay Press, 2001)
[6]A. W. Tozer, *The Knowledge of the Holy* (San Francisco: Harper & Row Publishers, 1961), 1.

Week Two

How the Mind Works

Last week we examined the interconnection between the mind, body, emotions, and spirit. Because we have the ability to change our thoughts, we can change how we feel and act. God made us with an infinite capacity to adapt and respond to new information and insights. I hope you are excited about the possibilities to change and grow as you begin your exploration of how the mind works.

 Psalm 100:3 is our Verse to Know this week. Read it along with Acts 17:24-25. Underline what God made according to these verses.

Circle what God gives all of us (v. 25).

When Paul was in Athens, he reasoned in the synagogue with Jews and those Greeks who had adopted the Jewish faith. He also spoke with Greek philosophers in the marketplace (Acts 17:16-18). In the verses from Acts you read part of what Paul said to these philosophers. God had made them and given them life. Although through the centuries we have learned things unknown to the New Testament world, nothing contradicts what Paul already knew. God made us, and our discoveries point to His astonishing work.

Take a minute to consider how you have been constructed. The design of your body is functional and complex. Each part has been carefully placed by God with purpose and love.

 Are you able to thank God for making you? Do you value His design and craftsmanship in uniquely creating you in His image? (circle)   yes   no

If so, pause to say a prayer of thanks. If not, ask God to give you an appreciation for your special place in His heart.

This week we will be looking at two characteristics of the mind: the physiology of the brain and the idea of personality.

THE PHYSIOLOGY OF THE BRAIN

How do thoughts get formed? Exactly what is going on in my head when I think about something? We do not need a detailed study of anatomy to understand how our brains work.

The Mind/Body Connection

Take a minute to think about how thoughts direct the activities of your body. Suppose a hot serving bowl is placed on the table. Reaching out, you take hold of the bowl so you can serve yourself. Your hand sends a rapid message to your brain, and your brain sends a message to your hand: *Let go!*

It happens in an instant. The message is carried by way of many nerve cells. These cells carry messages from every place in the body to the brain. Nerves are arranged in specific patterns to facilitate our body's complex communication system. See a simplified picture of a neuron, or nerve cell, below. This picture shows the end of one nerve cell, the beginning of another, and the space between them.

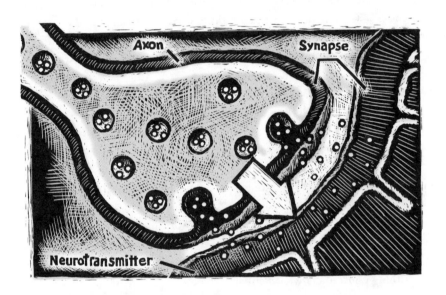

A message travels down the axon, or long part of the cell in the direction of the arrows. It is a bio-electrical signal. Notice that there is a space between the cells where they are not connected. This is the synapse—a junction between two nerve cells. As the message reaches the end of the axon, chemicals called neurotransmitters travel across the space (synapse). These chemicals are received by receptors on that part of the opposite cell, which is called the dendrite. The next nerve cell is stimulated to pick up the message and carry it down the line. This process is repeated between many cells in a very quick progression.

Thoughts are actually the combined working of billions of cells. It is easy to see the close connection between mind and body. Thoughts are actually physical in nature and control the body. The body in turn sends messages to the mind. This process sounds very mechanical, doesn't it? In fact, secular philosophers throughout history have conceptualized people as machines.[1]

Professor Phitt says:
Food for thought—yes, it really is true. Antioxidants boost intellectual power and aid emotional well-being. The top five antioxidant food choices are prunes, raisins, blueberries, blackberries, and garlic.

People are far more than machines. God created us with spirits. Paul explained to the Christians at Corinth that each person has a spirit, and in addition, God gives His Spirit to believers. Read 1 Corinthians 2:11-12 in the margin.

Thoughts are produced by the complex process of billions of cells working in the brain. But amazingly, we are spiritual beings capable of receiving God's Spirit within us. The Holy Spirit enables our minds to understand God's will and to communicate with Him. God has given us the ability to love Him with all our minds. No wonder David concluded, "Such knowledge is too wonderful for me, too lofty for me to attain" (Ps. 139:6).

Consider the fact that God has carefully made your mind. We scarcely understand the basic processes of the mind. But what little we can grasp is awe-inspiring and astonishing. Give thanks for how wonderfully you are created and how you can use your mind without needing to know every detail of how it works.

 Read Psalm 139:13-14 in the margin. Say it to God as a prayer.

HOW WE LEARN

Our minds not only react to things in the present but also learn for the future. Over the past 20 years, individuals who study learning have used the computer as an illustration to study and discuss the way the brain works.[2] As you can see in the illustration below, information and ideas enter a computer through the keyboard into the random access, or working, memory. From there information can be stored long-term on the hard drive for future use.

| **Keyboard** | **Random Access** | **Hard Disk** |
| Information and Ideas | (Working Memory) | (Long-Term Storage) |

Look at the illustration above. You can see how the brain follows a similar pattern. Sense perceptions are taken in and placed in short-term memory and then stored in long-term memory for future use. This storage of memories and how we retrieve and use them constitute the learning process.

| **Sense Perceptions** | **Short-Term Memory** | **Long-Term Memory** |
| (Hear, see, touch, taste, smell) | | |

"Who among men knows the thoughts of a man except the man's spirit within him? In the same way no one knows the thoughts of God except the Spirit of God. We have not received the spirit of the world but the Spirit who is from God, that we may understand what God has freely given us."
—1 Corinthians 2:11-12

"You created my
   inmost being;
   you knit me together in
   my mother's womb.
I praise you because I am
   fearfully and wonder-
   fully made;
   your works are wonderful,
I know that full well."
   —Psalm 139:13-14

Much of the *Fit 4* *Christian Wellness Plan* involves learning new things but also unlearning old thoughts, attitudes, and behaviors. As you look at the simple illustration of how the brain works on page 17, one of the first things to grasp is that learning begins by entering data.

 What data do you take into your mind that might be considered unhealthy or unproductive? Record it on the chart below, according to how it is taken in by your five senses. (Some sensory data may have more relevance to you than others. Tasting and smelling are probably linked with eating.) Second, record on the next line healthy data that can replace the unhealthy. I've given you an example of smell.

Sense Perceptions (What I Take In)	Short-Term (Working) Memory	Long-Term Memory
Hearing (unhealthy)		
(healthy)		
Seeing (unhealthy)		
(healthy)		
Touching (unhealthy)		
(healthy)		
Tasting (unhealthy)		
(healthy)		
Smelling (unhealthy) Being drawn in by smells of a doughnut shop.		
(healthy) Odor of freshly mowed green grass.		

Thankfully, God as Creator knows how our minds work. He is the One who best knows how we each can utilize our minds in a healthy and godly way. He teaches us how to think and how to avoid the obstacles that can block a successful life. Next week we will begin to examine the characteristics of those who love God with all their minds and how to overcome the obstacles that can get in the way.

THE IDEA OF PERSONALITY

God not only created us to think but also fashioned us as unique individuals. All of us have our own personalities. Personality cannot be separated from the way a person thinks. As a professor, I look out at a new class with the start of each semester. Some students are new; others have been with me in previous classes. On opening day the new students are just faces, but as the semester progresses, I begin to learn a small part of what makes each one unique. I see the clothes they like to wear; I learn whether they arrive early or late. Are they talkative or quiet? Do they appear nervous or relaxed at test time? Do they like my subject matter or do their interests lie elsewhere? All of these characteristics are aspects of personality.

Personality is best defined as traits that underlie behavior. In other words, what are the inner characteristics that produce the outer actions? Personality has a lot to do with how God created us. Earlier we saw how David affirmed this truth, "For you created my inmost being; you knit me together in my mother's womb" (Ps. 139:13). Perhaps you have heard mothers report that one of their children was more active and lively in the womb. Most parents who have more than one child are able to see personality differences almost immediately after birth.

 Which of the following two shapers of personality are most important in the development of a person? Circle one answer for each.

1. God-given traits/temperament   Most Important   About the Same   Least Important

2. How a person is reared   Most Important   About the Same   Least Important

GOD-GIVEN TRAITS/TEMPERAMENT

Understanding that God is the giver of our temperaments can take a great burden off of us. If our general make-up is from Him, we can give ourselves back to Him without hesitation or shame. Consider the apostle Paul. When we first met him in the Book of Acts, he was attempting to destroy Christianity. But after he became a Christian, he was a great church starter. "The weapons of destruction were turned into weapons of construction. The engine was reversed, and the direction changed; but it remained the same engine, and its power was increased under the new inspiration."[3]

The fact that Paul was energetic and relentless before he became a Christian, as well as energetic and relentless after giving his life to Christ, tells us something. Paul's intensity was a God-given trait, but Paul decided whether to use it for good or bad purposes.

You may have reversed your "engine" a long time ago, or you may just recently have given yourself to God and His purposes. The *Fit 4 Christian Wellness Plan* is based on having your engine running as God intended it to run when He made you. Our spiritual journey is the process of growing in loving the Lord our God with all our hearts, souls, minds, and strength.

If you have been wanting a personal relationship with God but were uncertain how to establish it, read the information on page 87 of this workbook. You will discover what it means to know God through Jesus Christ and how to become a Christian.

You will also find information on how to nurture this new relationship with God through Christ.

Some of us are more aware of our personality traits than others. Perhaps you are not noted for deep introspection. You may have never really stopped to analyze your personality.

 For the following opposite characteristics, place an *X* on the line to indicate your usual tendency. On this scale there is no good or bad, right or wrong. These are simply ideas of who you are as God made you.

Quiet/Listener	Talkative
Passive	Aggressive
Reserved	Outgoing
Dependent	Independent
Follower	Leader
Likes routine	Spontaneous
Spectator	Participant
Relies on feelings	Relies on facts

As you look at this sample of personality characteristics, think about how many combinations could be made just from this short list. Expand the list further and you get an idea of the variety to be found in the world of people we relate to every day. One of our goals in this study will be to gain a better understanding of our uniqueness, so we can learn to be more successful in loving God with all our hearts, souls, minds, and strength.

The Bible illustrates the variety of personalities. We view David's passion, Hannah's devotion, Elijah's boldness, and Esther's courage. Peter is quick to jump off a boat into the sea and equally quick to put his foot in his mouth (Matt. 14:22-36; 16:21-23)! Peter and John are often together in the Book of Acts, but Peter does all the preaching, and John is mostly silent (Acts 2:14-36; 3:11-26). Yet, John later wrote the Gospel of John, the Books of First, Second, and Third John, and Revelation—five books of the New Testament!

I am a person who much prefers routine to spontaneous living. As a result, I try to maintain a fairly organized schedule. I know this is how God made me and will best use me. However, I have friends who are much more spontaneous by nature. If they attempt to operate on too tight of a schedule, they are less effective in their service for God.

OUTREACH

You have just drawn a picture of yourself. Can you think of other traits that describe you? How does self-awareness help us relate better to others? Write your ideas below.

Of course, at times God calls lovers-of-routine to be spontaneous and spontaneous types to develop a schedule! We are all capable of making adjustments and should be able to flex when needed. This flexibility is an important ingredient in dealing with life's stressors. It is also essential in relationships. A married man cannot say to his new wife, *God made me as a quiet person, and I don't have to talk to you.* Instead, he must be willing to open up to his wife, although that does not come naturally. Otherwise, the quality of their relationship will deteriorate.

Next we want to look at the second major influence that shapes our personalities: how we were reared. Our background includes both our families of origin and our life experiences.

HOW A PERSON IS REARED

We each have our God-given temperament, but our personalities can also be affected by how we were reared. Researchers call this the nature/nurture debate. Nature refers to how God made us. Nurture refers to family influences and our personal life experiences.

Family Influences

God gives parents a wonderful opportunity to influence their children. Some people reflect on their earliest memories with joy and appreciation for the care and love extended to them. For others, thoughts of childhood are rather mixed, if not filled with pain. Because God knows the effect that parents will have on children, He outlines their responsibilities in Deuteronomy 6:4-7.

> "Hear, O Israel: The Lord our God, the Lord is one. Love the Lord your God with all your heart and with all your soul and with all your strength. These commandments that I give you today are to be upon your hearts. Impress them on your children. Talk about them when you sit at home and when you walk along the road, when you lie down and when you get up." —Deuteronomy 6:4-7

God knows that children will grow up to become responsible adults when parents put God and His Word first in their own lives (vv. 4-6) and when they teach the Bible to their children (v. 7).

Place a check by the word that best describes the home in which you were reared.

1. God came first in my family. ❑ Yes ❑ Sometimes ❑ No
2. God's Word was central to the life of my family. ❑ Yes ❑ Sometimes ❑ No
3. My parents sought to teach the Bible to me. ❑ Yes ❑ Sometimes ❑ No

UPREACH

Have you learned the **Fit 4** theme verses from Mark 12:30-31 (see page 8). If not, determine to learn them as a way of reminding yourself to put God first in your life.

Statistically, children reared in an environment where God was honored and church played an important role in the family's life will tend to reproduce this type of lifestyle in their homes as adults. If God was not first in your family, you may have some catching up to do, but you can give Him priority now, whether your family consists of one or several persons. You may need to lead the way by word and example. Recall that the **Fit 4** theme verse, Mark 12:30, begins with Jesus' reminder to love God first.

In addition to supplying a child with a strong religious heritage, wise parents will also nurture a loving relationship. A newborn comes into the world with some very important needs: to be held, to be loved, and to be cared for. The importance of touch for the well-being of infants is well documented in medical journals. In fact, the best way to help a baby to stop crying is simply to pick her up! The need for warmth and touch extends throughout life, and the best climate for growth and learning in children develops from a strong emotional attachment with parents. However, the most important factor is not how the child responds to parents but how the parent responds to the child.

Children who feel warmly attached to parents are more likely to be emotionally secure, compliant, eager for challenging tasks, and attentive. Theodore Roosevelt had this to say about the importance of parental devotion:

> We cannot as a Nation get along at all if we haven't the right kind of home life. Such a life is not only the supreme duty, but also the supreme reward of duty. Every rightly constituted woman or man, if she or he is worth his or her salt, must feel that there is no such ample reward to be found anywhere in life as the reward of children, the reward of a happy family life.[4]

Again, consider how you were reared. Place a check by the word that best describes your experience in the family.

My parents extended warmth and hugged me.	❑ Often	❑ Sometimes	❑ Rarely
My mother said she loved me.	❑ Often	❑ Sometimes	❑ Rarely
My father said he loved me.	❑ Often	❑ Sometimes	❑ Rarely
My mother seemed to understand me.	❑ Often	❑ Sometimes	❑ Rarely
My father seemed to understand me.	❑ Often	❑ Sometimes	❑ Rarely

Ideally, parents need to carefully balance affection and discipline. The key word for *discipline* in the Old Testament is *yasar*. It means to instruct or correct.[5] Parents can know that they are approaching discipline with the right heart attitude when they are seeking to provide instruction as the motive of discipline.

The negative effects of poor parenting will be covered in detail in week 6. Many of you look back on your growing-up years with fond memories. But if your experiences leave you troubled and saddened, I would recommend the study, *Making Peace With Your Past.*[6]

Life Experiences

While the effects of parenting are important, the life experiences that we face and how we respond to them will also play an important role in shaping our personalities. If you moved around often as a child, you may be more open to change than another person who lived in the same town all of his life. Persons who grew up in an environment that encouraged artistic expression may find it easier to express themselves in creative ways.

A person traumatized by a house fire as a child may always fear fire, but the event doesn't have to keep her from buying a house with a fireplace. Recovery stories from those who experienced childhood sexual, emotional, or physical abuse assure us that life experiences do not have to determine our futures.

Many people have found it helpful to think back over the pivotal events in their lives and ask themselves the question, *How did this event shape who I am today?* Throughout the Bible we read of significant ages or crossroads in a person's life in which new experiences were opened to them and consequently more was expected of them. At age 12 Jewish children became responsible as adults in their relationship to God. At this age Jesus went to the temple, listened to the teachers, and asked them questions (Luke 2:41-52). At age 20 Hebrew youths were able to go to war (Num. 1:2-3), and at age 30 they were able to work in the tent of meeting (Num. 4:2-4). At age 30, David became king (2 Sam. 5:3-4), and Jesus began His ministry (Luke 3:23).

 Think about your important life experiences at these three ages. Take a moment to note these experiences. How did these experiences shape who you are today?

	IMPORTANT EXPERIENCE	FEELINGS AT THAT TIME
Age 12	_____	_____
	_____	_____
Age 20	_____	_____
	_____	_____
Age 30	_____	_____
	_____	_____

INREACH

Reread this week's Verse to Know on page 15. You belong to God and He cares for you as a loving shepherd cares for His sheep. You can trust Him with every life experience. As you think about pivotal events from your past, have you learned to take life's lemons and make lemonade? How do you think people manage to make a positive out of a negative? Read Romans 8:28 as you consider your answer.

Because God made us with the capacity to change, past experiences do not have to determine our future. We can learn from the negative experiences and choose to use them as character builders or we can let them sabotage our lives from now on. The Bible offers us pictures of both types of characters: those who let the past defeat them and those who used the lemons of life to make lemonade.

Joseph, one of the twelve sons of Jacob, was sold as a slave by his jealous brothers and then falsely accused and imprisoned by his captor. After years of languishing in an Egyptian jail, he was finally released. Eventually, he became the second in command to the Pharaoh. When Joseph's brothers came to Egypt to buy grain, Joseph revealed his identity. The brothers feared for their lives.

If you had been Joseph, would you have sought revenge? ❑ yes ❑ no

Read Joseph's response in Genesis 50:19-21. How did Joseph turn a negative life experience into a blessing?

_____

_____

One of the roles I enjoy is that of a sports psychologist. I am fascinated by how a person's past experiences and mental approach to life can influence performance. The best athlete does not always win the gold medal. A less talented athlete may have more determination. Likewise, experience is key in the playoffs. Often, the effect of having "been there, done that" outweighs the talent of the other team.

Your success with fitness and nutrition can be enhanced by focusing on gaining experiences of success. For example, if you begin walking, start slowly (walking one mile, as opposed to walking five). Positive experiences provide confidence and a foundation for future growth. Your small successes will be enhanced by your focus on Christ—"I can do everything through him who gives me strength" (Phil. 4:13).

[1] David Hothersall, *History of Psychology* (New York: Random House, 1984), 30.

[2] William R. Yount, *Created to Learn* (Nashville: Broadman & Holman Publishers, 1996), 209-230.

[3] Philip Schaff, *History of the Christian Church* (Grand Rapids, MI: Wm. B. Eerdmans Publishing Company, 1985), 287.

[4] Theodore Roosevelt in an address before the First International Congress in America on the welfare of the child, March 1908. From Chuck Swindoll, *The Strong Family* (Portland, OR: Multnomah Press, 1991), 78.

[5] Spiros Zodhiates et al., eds., *The Complete Word Study Old Testament* (Chattanooga, TN: AMG Publishers, 1994), 50.

[6] Tim Sledge, *Making Peace with Your Past* (Nashville: LifeWay Press, 1992).

Week Three

A Thinking and Growing Christian

When Tim began his first semester at a large university, he had an experience that challenged his faith and propelled him toward the greatest growing experience of his life. His world history professor, an intelligent and articulate man, argued that Christianity had been the greatest hindrance to intellectual growth in the Western world. With each class he offered new material to substantiate his claim. Several weeks into the semester, Tim sat in the library with a look of dejection. His professor was clear in his arguments, and although Tim felt the assertions were one-sided, he had trouble dismissing all that his professor had said. Would he hinder his own intellectual growth by keeping a tight hold on his Christian beliefs?

Tim remained mired in his troubled thoughts for about a week. But when he had the chance to talk with several other Christians in his dormitory, together they decided to explore the matter in a Bible study. They would meet each week for the remainder of the school year. No intellectual rock would be left unturned; no idea swept under the carpet. In addition to the Bible, they committed to reading great Christian writers and studying Bible commentaries and resource material.

What resulted proved to be a fresh love for learning and a new commitment to Christ and the Scriptures. Tim and his four friends prayed and sought God for wisdom. They learned to view the world through the teachings of the Bible, adopting as a theme for their study, "All truth is God's truth." At the end of Tim's freshman year, he and his friends each committed to continuing their quest. They hoped to divide their group the following year into two studies to include others. In addition to growing as Christians, each of the young men maintained a high academic standing.

 Perhaps you have faced a similar experience when you were challenged by someone to defend your faith. If so, what was your response?

_____

_____

VERSE TO KNOW

" 'Who has known the mind of the Lord that he may instruct him?' But we have the mind of Christ."
—1 Corinthians 2:16

Like Tim and his friends, many Christians struggle with similar questions in their search for truth. Those who have school-aged children have concerns for what their children are being taught. They wonder how they can pass on the rich heritage of their faith to children constantly bombarded by the world's values. The answers Tim and his friends found are at the heart of this study: loving God with all of our minds.

As we reflect on the calling to love God with all our minds, the remainder of this study will be divided into three sections. In the first section, weeks 3 and 4, we will explore mental fitness. What are the characteristics or marks of persons who love the Lord with all their minds? In weeks 5 and 6, we will discuss what hinders us from loving God with all our minds. In our third section, weeks 7, 8, and 9, we will consider how we go about changing our thinking. What is the process of reconstruction, change, and growth that God has given us?

Our Verse to Know for this week tells us that "we have the mind of Christ" (1 Cor. 2:16). This important truth was a confidence builder for Paul. He had the difficult task of working with a group of people who took great pride in everything they knew. "The Corinthians were infected with something of the spirit of nearby Athens. They fancied themselves as thinkers and took great pride in their supposed intellectual superiority."[1]

Paul was well aware that people enjoy the acquiring of knowledge, but he also knew that to keep people centered on godly wisdom, he would need to refer them frequently to the Giver of their wisdom. People who are characterized by loving God with all their minds realize that they must maintain a balance between a healthy hunger to learn and arrogance in their attainments.

SEEKING GODLY WISDOM

Just prior to telling the Corinthians that they had the mind of Christ, Paul reminded them that what they know and understand concerning God, His work, and His gifts was made known to them by the Holy Spirit. Paul said, "We have not received the spirit of the world but the Spirit who is from God, that we may understand what God has freely given us" (1 Cor. 2:12).

In a similar reminder, Jesus told His disciples that although He was leaving to be with the Father, they would be receiving the Spirit as teacher.

 Read John 16:13-14 in the margin.
Into what will the Spirit guide us (John 16:13)?

_____

The Spirit makes God's truth known to us. List ways God has revealed His truth to you.

_____

"The fear of the Lord is the beginning of wisdom, and knowledge of the Holy One is understanding."
—Proverbs 9:10

" 'When he, the Spirit of truth, comes, he will guide you into all truth. He will not speak on his own; he will speak only what he hears, and he will tell you what is yet to come. He will bring glory to me by taking from what is mine and making it known to you.' "
—John 16:13-14

Centuries before Jesus revealed to His disciples the Source of truth, Solomon encouraged his readers to seek after godly wisdom. Read Solomon's words in Proverbs 2:3-6.

The first step in our quest for wisdom has everything to do with assessing our own desire to know. How motivated are we to seek truth? Recall the account of one of Tim's first university classes on page 25. As Tim wrestled with his professor's remarks, a small flame was kindled deep within him. He and his friends began to do what Solomon says. They began to "call out for insight and cry aloud for understanding." They looked for it "as for silver," and searched for it "as for hidden treasure." The result for them (and for you and me if we take the opportunity) was a personal discovery that "the Lord gives wisdom, and from his mouth come knowledge and understanding." The call to seek after God's wisdom became a personal call to Tim and his friends.

What can you do today to accept Solomon's challenge to seek wisdom and understanding? Check all that apply.

❑ Seek godly companions.
❑ Read a book.
❑ Visit a Christian book store.
❑ Keep going to a Bible study.
❑ Talk to your pastor.
❑ Start a Bible study.
❑ Pray for insight and understanding.
❑ Join a Bible study.

Can you think of two books that would increase your store of godly wisdom and that you would like to read? Record the titles and a target date for starting.

Title _____ Target Date _____

_____ _____

_____ _____

The first characteristic of persons who love God with all their minds is that they have a desire to seek godly wisdom. God promises that the one who passionately looks for wisdom will be happily rewarded. Paul told the Corinthians that we have received God's Spirit in order to understand what God has freely given us (1 Cor. 2:12). He earnestly desires for us to have His wisdom.

This quest for wisdom and understanding is related to what is often described as our worldview. The second characteristic of persons who love God with all their minds is that they are thinking Christians and have a biblical worldview. Let's take a moment to understand what we mean by *worldview*.

"If you call out for insight
and cry aloud for
understanding,
and if you look for it as
for silver
and search for it as for
hidden treasure,
then you will understand the
fear of the Lord
and find the knowledge
of God.
For the Lord gives wisdom,
and from his mouth come
knowledge and
understanding."
—Proverbs 2:3-6

The first characteristic of persons who love God with all their minds is that they have a desire to seek godly wisdom.

The second characteristic is that they are thinking Christians and have a biblical worldview.

LIVING AS A THINKING CHRISTIAN

Prior to the great age of exploration, every ship captain understood that the world was flat. With uncertainty as to where the earth ended, captains worked hard to sail within sight of land!

When the earth was finally circumnavigated, ideas concerning the nature of the planet we live on changed. A round earth, as well as other discoveries of that age, required people to make adjustments in their understanding of the world. Christian thinkers were forced to reconcile a difficult problem. In Genesis 1–2, the Bible presents the creation of humankind as the center of all His created works. But if the earth rotates around the sun, had humanity lost its central position in the universe? Most of us would argue that the universe as we now know it does not challenge the Bible's account of creation. Yet, the first reaction of the Roman Catholic Church was to turn its back on the advances of science.

Perhaps the best example of this reaction can be seen in what happened with Galileo and his telescope. Galileo's proof for the Copernican theory of the universe, stating that the earth moves around the sun, relied on his invention of the telescope. Yet, amazingly, Copernicus waited until his deathbed to publish his works, and Galileo, who furthered the work of Copernicus, had to withdraw his findings or face imprisonment. They were not in conflict with the teaching of the Bible, but they were in conflict with the worldview of their time, which looked back to the teaching of Aristotle for their understanding of science and the world.

Despite the unfavorable climate for intellectual pursuits, Copernicus and Galileo helped us to expand our understanding of the universe, and, in turn, we are better able to give glory to God who has "marked off the heavens" (Isa. 40:12).

As Christians, we should not be afraid to explore the world around us. We can have a confidence that new discoveries will only work for God's glory, as they demonstrate His wisdom and greatness. God wants us to explore, uncover, and think about His creation. He encourages us to ask, "Why did He choose to do it this way? What is His purpose for us in this new knowledge?"

Instead of turning our backs on new inventions and discoveries, we need a Christian worldview. Charles Colson and Nancy Pearcey explain in their book, *How Now Shall We Live?*, that "genuine Christianity is a way of seeing and comprehending *all* reality. It is a worldview."[2] In other words, just as biblical Christianity answers the questions of salvation and spiritual growth, it also encourages us to understand the world around us. The science and engineering that enabled ships to travel to distant lands would later bring missionaries to those faraway places.

What is a biblical worldview? Is the way Christians view life and the world around us really any different from the perspective of secular thinkers? It is. This difference can be seen in the three questions that any worldview must answer. First, where did we come from, and who are we? Second, what has gone wrong with the world? And third, what can we do to fix it?[3] Let's look at a simple chart that contrasts Christian and secular worldviews.

CONTRASTS IN WORLDVIEW

Question	Christian Worldview	Secular Worldview
Where did we come from and who are we?	We are created by God in His image.	We evolved from lower life forms.
What has gone wrong with the world?	Humankind has fallen because of sin.	The social environment has failed us.
What can we do to fix it?	We must find redemption through Jesus Christ.	We must continue to evolve and promote social justice.

Does American culture today most reflect the worldview of Christians or of secularists? (circle)

Christians   Secularists

Explain the difference it would make in how you live your life if you answered the following questions according to the secularists' viewpoint.

1. Where did we come from?

_____

_____

2. What has gone wrong?

_____

_____

3. What can we do to fix it?

_____

_____

The third characteristic of Christians who love God with all their minds is the desire to learn and grow.

"It is the glory of God to conceal a matter; to search out a matter is the glory of kings."
—Proverbs 25:2

You may have noted that the secularists' viewpoint generally leads to despair as individuals find they have no inherent value (we evolved from lower life forms), no ultimate purpose except survival, and no hope to offer others. Secularists can change public policy but they have no means to change the human heart. On the other hand, a Christian worldview teaches us that we are made in God's image according to His design. He gives us not only purpose for our lives but also a guidebook, the Bible, that explains how to live according to God's design. He covered our sin problem with the blood of His Son, Jesus, and is preparing a heavenly home for us. Jesus commanded us to share this good news with the world (Matt. 28:19-20). Instead of despair, we have hope to offer others.

Throughout history, Christians have faced challenging questions from those who claimed that Christianity is based on faith and not fact. Scientific and archeological studies have confirmed many facts that substantiate our faith. However, the secular worldview is also a faith supposition. It takes a lot of faith to believe that billions of years ago our universe was created by an accidental explosion that resulted in the precise and orderly natural world we enjoy.

Both faith and intellectual effort are required to find suitable answers to the skeptics' claims. We need the same two ingredients daily: faith in God and His Word and intellectual effort. The third characteristic of Christians who love God with all their minds is the desire to learn and grow.

CONTINUING TO LEARN AND GROW

Christians must think and learn because God desires growth for us. We have a God-given curiosity about how the world operates. God made us and the world in which we live dependent upon our creative solutions to problems we face. Copernicus, the 15th-century astronomer who determined that the earth moved around the sun, believed it made simpler mathematical sense. "And since Copernicus was convinced that God had made the world mathematically precise, getting better formulas was good enough for him … Copernicus was inspired not by the scientific facts available to him but by his Christian faith."[4]

1. God's greatness is revealed in what He has hidden. According to Proverbs 25:2, God has actually concealed, or hidden, numerous things from us. He left many things to be discovered to further reveal His power and greatness. In such areas as medicine and technology, discoveries of antibiotics, various heart and cancer treatments, and organ transplants are among the many advances of the last one hundred years. Research continues in many areas, and with each new discovery, men and women uncover another aspect of the glory of God.

2. Our greatness is revealed in what we discover. We are encouraged to search out the wonders of God's creation. At the very beginning of creation in the garden of Eden, God brought to Adam the birds and animals that He had made "to see what he would name them; and whatever the man called each living creature, that was its name" (Gen. 2:19). This task was not simple. Adam would need to examine each animal carefully to find distinguishing characteristics and qualities. He learned the joy and fascination of making new discoveries, using to the fullest the energies of his mind.

The Hebrew word *glory* actually has to do with heaviness or weight.[5] As a person begins to investigate and ponder God's creation and to discover the beneficial things that can be used, that person grows in stature. Inventors and innovators from the past are highly regarded because their work has benefited others.

Scripture warns of leaving God out of our quest for knowledge, but it never encourages us to narrow the extent of our learning as long as we are pursuing God's truth. Surely, it goes without saying that we are not to pursue knowledge of certain topics that bring dishonor to God. Read 1 Thessalonians 5:21-22.

The Bible commends both Moses and Daniel for the breadth of their education. Consider the verses in the margin.

> "Moses was educated in all the wisdom of the Egyptians and was powerful in speech and action."
> —Acts 7:22

How would you evaluate the cultures of Egypt and Babylon? Mark an X at the appropriate point on the line.

_____

godly   ungodly

Why do you think Moses was educated in the learning of the Egyptians and Daniel was exposed to the literature, language, and wisdom of Babylon?

_____

_____

_____

> "The king ordered Ashpenaz … to teach them the language and literature of the Babylonians. … To these four young men God gave knowledge and understanding of all kinds of literature and learning. And Daniel could understand visions and dreams of all kinds."
> —Daniel 1:3-4,17

God preserved Moses through the action of Pharaoh's daughter when he was an infant. God planned that this great leader would know and understand the culture in which he lived. When he returned to Egypt to deliver the Israelites from captivity, he was well acquainted with the Pharaoh and his palace. God gave Daniel and his friends knowledge and understanding as they studied in Babylon. At the conclusion of their training, they were brought before the king, who found them "ten times better than all the magicians and enchanters in his whole kingdom" (Dan. 1:20). Make a commitment to the Lord to grow and learn for the rest of your life. He will steer you in a direction that honors Him.

What value do you place on education?

❏ A little   ❏ Some   ❏ A lot

What factors have influenced your attitudes toward education? (circle)

family   culture   church   friends   personality   teachers

What future actions will demonstrate that you are committed to learning and growing?

_____

_____

Professor Phitt says:
As you think about enrolling in adult education classes, consider the possibilities of classes at your local gym or club such as aerobics, swimming, golf, or handball. These classes not only stimulate your mind but improve your level of physical fitness as well.

If education was not valued in your family, or you chose to treat your educational opportunities with indifference, remember that it is never too late to become a lifelong learner. Many communities with a community college or other institutions of higher learning offer adult education classes. You can get your GED, an associate degree, or enroll in a four-year college. College classes are now offered on the Internet, as well.

Technical institutions can teach you everything from interior decorating to the latest computer technology. Adult education classes are offered by hospitals, libraries, schools, and churches. Many adults choose to study a foreign language, take up oil painting, or enroll in other courses that teach them basic life skills.

If you do not enjoy reading, consider making a commitment to listening to books on tape as you commute to work or as you complete chores around the house. If you do not like reading the daily newspaper, listen to the evening news. If you learn by doing, sign up for a course that gives you hands-on experience, such as cooking or auto mechanics.

Consider what it says about you if you do not have a goal to learn a new skill or acquire new knowledge over the next calendar year. Could you truthfully say you already know all you need to know to keep functioning at the same level indefinitely? Our world changes daily, and we must change in response to it.

AVOIDING ARROGANCE

As we noted on page 26, we must maintain a balance between a healthy hunger to learn and arrogance in our attainments. From the beginning, mankind has wanted to be like God and know all that He knows. In the garden of Eden, the serpent tempted Eve by saying, "God knows that when you eat of it your eyes will be opened, and you will be like God, knowing good and evil" (Gen. 3:5).

In Genesis 11 mankind's arrogance appears again when the people said to themselves, "let us build ourselves a city, with a tower that reaches to the heavens, so that we may make a name for ourselves and not be scattered over the face of the whole earth" (Gen. 11:4). By the time of the Judges, the author simply closes the book with this sentence: "every man did that which was right in his own eyes" (Judges 21:25, KJV).

The remainder of the Bible offers account after account of mankind's attempts to outwit God and each other. When Jesus ministered here on earth, He warned, " 'False Christs and false prophets will appear and perform great signs and miracles to deceive even the elect—if that were possible' " (Matt. 24:24). Jesus' message was quite different from the world's message. Read Matthew 20:25-27 in the margin.

 Write words or phrases to describe the difference between a spirit of arrogance and a spirit of humility.

Arrogance	Humility

"Jesus called them together and said, 'You know that the rulers of the Gentiles lord it over them, and their high officials exercise authority over them. Not so with you. Instead, whoever wants to become great among you must be your servant, and whoever wants to be first must be your slave.' "
—Matthew 20:25-27

Humility is not low self-esteem. Humility is recognizing the greatness of God and yielding to His authority in our lives. When we understand ourselves in relation to almighty God, we will not be tempted to be prideful in our accomplishments. Rather, we will thank Him for giving us the abilities, the knowledge, and the wisdom to use them appropriately.

MENTAL FITNESS

As we close this week's study, reread the Verse to Know from 1 Corinthians 2:16. Can you say it from memory? It reminds us that "we have the mind of Christ." In his book, *The Mind of Christ*, T. W. Hunt says, "God is more anxious for you to have the mind of Christ than you are. Tell God you are willing for Him to change you. He will do what you ask, because conforming you to the image of Christ is His will."[6]

 Take a moment to pray along with me.

Father, thank You for giving me Your Holy Spirit so that I can understand all that You have given to me. Please increase my desire to seek godly wisdom. Help me to see the world through the truth that You have displayed for me in the Bible. I want to be a thinking Christian who will understand and impact the world around me. Thank You for encouraging me this week to learn and grow. I give You my mind along with my heart, soul, and strength for Your good purposes. Amen.

UPREACH
Tell God that you desire the mind of Christ. Commit yourself to learning from the world's greatest Teacher.

Our words and our actions will never be more Christlike than our minds, because they originate in our thoughts.

Christlikeness is God's goal for you and me. Our words and our actions will never be more Christlike than our minds, because they originate in our thoughts. Godly thoughts, in turn, result from setting our minds on "things above" (Col. 3:2) and renewing our minds (Rom. 12:2) as a continual process. "If our will is set and our mind has grown through constant renewal, we will be qualified for any test God allows to come our way."[7]

As we close today's study, can you fill in the blanks to recall the three characteristics of persons who love God with all their minds?

1. They have a desire to seek _____ _____.

2. They are _____ Christians and have a biblical

_____.

3. They desire to _____ and _____.

[1]Donald Guthrie & Stephen Motyer, "The Letters," *Zondervan Handbook to the Bible,* 3rd edition, ed. Pat and David Alexander (Grand Rapids, MI: Zondervan Publishing House, 1999), 698.

[2]Charles Colson & Nancy Pearcy, *How Now Shall We Live?* (Wheaton, IL: Tyndale House Publishers, Inc., 1999), 15.

[3]Ibid., xiii.

[4]Ibid., 425.

[5]Spiros Zodhiates et al., eds., *The Complete Word Study Old Testament* (Chattanooga, TN: AMG Publishers, 1994), 54.

[6]T.W. Hunt, *The Mind of Christ* (Nashville: Broadman & Holman Publishers, 1995), 16.

[7]Ibid., 15.

Week Four
A Healthy, Loving Christian

Cindy knew she needed to lose weight. Along with several good friends, she joined a group that offered a sensible plan of exercise and proper nutrition. After 18 months, Cindy reached her personal goal. She had shed 85 pounds! Her experience contained some of the usual ups and downs along the way. In fact, some weeks she lost nothing or even gained a little. Along the way she faced some significant emotional factors—her husband changed jobs, one of her sons required a tutor, and her sister was diagnosed with cancer. (Cindy continues to pray and offer support, and her sister's prognosis is good). Through it all, Cindy was able to keep going and reach her goal.

However, Cindy continued to confront a perplexing question. How could a woman who had lost 85 pounds still view herself as fat? Her husband praised her, and her daughter told her that she was the prettiest mom at the 5th grade class open house. So why did all the self-doubting continue? She was tempted to try to lose more, but her doctor told her that she had reached a healthy weight. A friend in college had struggled with anorexia, so Cindy reminded herself of that danger. And yet, why wasn't she able to see herself as others apparently did? We will attempt to answer this and similar questions this week.

 Mental challenge: It may have been several days since you explored three characteristics of people who love the Lord with all their minds. Can you recall the characteristics? Oops! No fair looking at page 34!

1. They have a desire to seek godly _____.

2. They are _____ Christians and have a biblical

   _____.

3. They desire to _____ and _____.

This week we will examine three additional characteristics: have a healthy self-image, remember the importance of others, and maintain healthy boundaries.

HAVE A HEALTHY SELF-IMAGE

 Draw a picture of yourself in the frame. If you are not an artist, use words to describe yourself. What characteristics did you emphasize?

Cindy's baffling difficulty in changing her self-image is not unique. In fact, it is a fairly common concern for people, especially those who sincerely want to change for the better. Our self-image is formed early in life, and we carry it with us for the remainder of our lives unless something or Someone intervenes.

Memories are closely tied to emotions. Cindy had a long history of concerns surrounding her appearance. When she arrived at a healthy weight, negative feelings still lingered. It takes time to adjust to change, particularly when the change that has occurred involves an area associated with negative, self-doubting memories.

I have a friend whose mother often reminded him of what a shy, quiet child he had been. When my friend entered high school and took a drama elective, he found he could project a much more outgoing and engaging personality. This knowledge served him well when he entered the teaching profession.

 What messages about yourself did you receive as a child?

_____

Have you found it difficult to change negative messages? (circle)   yes   no

Do you think your present view of yourself is fixed, unchangeable? (circle)   yes   no

Because we have to play "catch up" with our emotions, our self-image does not change overnight. Within a biblical framework, we will continue to learn and grow as we seek godly wisdom on the subject. Individuals should continue in a group study as they work through the *Fit 4* plan, even after personal goals are reached. The group provides reinforcement for a new, more accurate self-image.

INREACH

Make it a goal to give yourself an honest compliment every day. Being pleased with something you have said or done or the way you look does not mean you are being prideful or arrogant. Can you explain the difference?

Keys to a Healthy Self-Image

What does a healthy view of ourselves look like? In other words, how does God want us to picture ourselves? If you were not encouraged toward a healthy self-image as a child, you may be surprised to find that growing a healthy view of self begins with developing your spiritual life. All the self-improvement programs in the world will not substitute for finding your identity and purpose in a personal relationship with God through Jesus Christ.

1. Grow in awareness of Jesus' love.

Our Verses to Know this week are found in Ephesians 3:17-19 (p. 35). Read this passage carefully. Paul wrote to tell the Christians in Ephesus that he was praying that God would help them understand how expansive the love of Christ was for each one of them. Paul knew the foundation for Christian growth and health—the love of Jesus for each believer. Christ's love for each believer is so great that Paul appeared to contradict himself. He prayed that God would give believers power to understand what passed their ability to understand: the love of Christ.

The first key to having a healthy view of ourselves is to grow in our understanding of Jesus Christ's love for us. His love is unconditional. You can't earn it because it is freely given. Although Jesus knows everything about you, He chose to die for you and will gladly welcome you to His home someday.

 Read Romans 8:38-39 in the margin. What has the power to separate us from God's love? (check) ❑ demons ❑ the future ❑ nothing

> "I am convinced that neither death nor life, neither angels nor demons, neither the present nor the future, nor any powers, neither height nor depth, nor anything else in all creation, will be able to separate us from the love of God that is in Christ Jesus our Lord."
> —Romans 8:38-39

2. Live by faith in Jesus Christ.

Read the words of Paul to the church at Galatia found in Galatians 2:20. All attempts at self-worth ultimately flow from our connection with the hub of the universe—Jesus Christ. Since I have been crucified with Christ and Christ lives in me, I now live my life by faith in Him.

 Read each of the following verses and draw a line to match the verses to a statement that demonstrates the importance of exercising faith in Jesus.

Colossians 1:15-17   Christ is the source of our peace.

Colossians 2:6-8   Christ holds all of life together.

Colossians 3:15-17   Christ keeps us from being deceived.

> "I have been crucified with Christ and I no longer live, but Christ lives in me. The life I live in the body, I live by faith in the Son of God, who loved me and gave himself for me."
> —Galatians 2:20

3. Live by the Word of God.

Our sense of worth often rises or falls based on how we are handling daily pressures. Most of us tend to gain control over one aspect of our lives only to see another aspect slipping through our hands. Consider the man who found that when his yard was finally in order, he had not been spending adequate time with his family. When that area of life was back under control, he noticed that the hedges around his house required trimming and the grass needed cutting!

> "Your word is a lamp to my feet and a light for my path."
> —Psalm 119:105

UPREACH

Reread this week's Verses
to Know on page 35.
How does knowing that God
loves you unconditionally
affect your self-image?

You may not be able to live each day in perfect balance; however, ask God to help you set aside time for reading His Word and praying. Give this time priority over any person or activity that stands in the way. Continually evaluate your life in the light of God's Word (Ps. 119:105). When we are living in obedience to God in His Spirit, we have His love, joy, peace, patience, kindness, goodness, faithfulness, gentleness, and self-control (Gal. 5:22-23). These attributes are amazingly productive in helping us to feel good about ourselves!

Let's return to Cindy's dilemma of not being able to enjoy reaching her weight-reduction goal. By observing the keys to a healthy self-image, Cindy will be able to take the focus off of an unhealthy preoccupation with her appearance and put it on God and His Word. He has promised to conform her to the image of Christ as she commits herself to pursuits that encourage growth and learning. God's unconditional love gives her status and worth. Authentic change is a gradual process, particularly when lifestyle habits are involved. The new birth as a Christian occurs in an instant, but growth in Christlikeness is a process.

REMEMBER THE IMPORTANCE OF OTHERS

In addition to having a healthy self-image, mentally fit individuals remember the importance of others. Instead of a self-focus, they develop an other-focus. *I heard Andrew was sick; I wonder what we can do to help? Sarah did a great job in the performance last week; I should give her a call and thank her.*

The attitude of Christians toward each other is a recurring theme in Paul's letters. Paul wrote to the Philippians, "Do nothing from selfishness or empty conceit, but with humility of mind let each of you regard one another as more important than himself" (Phil. 2:3, NASB). Paul wrote to the Christians at Rome encouraging them to be characterized by an attitude of humility toward one another. He wanted them to live with each other in an unassuming way. He wrote, "Be of the same mind toward one another; do not be haughty in mind, but associate with the lowly. Do not be wise in your own estimation" (Rom. 12:16, NASB).

 Think of persons you know who are characterized by "humility of mind" toward others. What is it about them that you admire?

OUTREACH

Fit 4 seeks to balance inreach with outreach as we continue our upreach to God. Rate yourself by placing an X on the following scale:

self-focused   other-focused

God has created us to live and grow side-by-side with other people. When Jesus agonized in the garden, He wanted others around Him. He said to His disciples, " 'Stay here and keep watch' " (Mark 14:34). When Paul was imprisoned at Rome, he asked Timothy to come quickly and to bring Mark with him (2 Tim. 4:9-11).

Supportive ties may or may not include family members. If possible, stay close to your family. In addition to family, when we meet regularly with good Christian friends, we are more likely to maintain a realistic outlook on life. Honest friends help us view ourselves in a more reasonable manner. As a result of their friendships, we are less likely to hold too high or too low a view of ourselves.

The problem with relationships is that they take time! In order to make time for family and friends, we must seek to live balanced lives. Balance does not indicate equal time for each aspect of life. You probably work an 8 hour day but spend only 45 minutes in exercise; however, both are important. Balance begins by establishing priorities, which flow from and need to be in keeping with the Word of God. A priority is defined as something that goes ahead of, or takes precedence over, something else. Consequently, when we say that something is of first priority, we mean that it takes importance over the rest of what we do. I would suggest the following order of importance as you seek balance.

1. Time with God
2. Time with Family
3. Time for Work
4. Time for Ministry
5. Time for Personal Renewal

 Put an X on the line to evaluate the degree of balance in your life.

_____

unbalanced   somewhat balanced   balanced

Are any of your priorities currently being neglected? (circle)   yes   no

Set specific goals that accomplish your life priorities or the specific plans that you intend to fulfill. When setting goals or helping others to do so, consider the simple tests of a good goal from the ***Fit 4** Nutrition Member Workbook* (see page 32).

S.M.A.R.T. Goals

- Specific: What exactly do I want to achieve?
- Measurable: When will I know I have reached my goal?
- Attainable: Can I really reach this goal?
- Realistic: Is this a wish or a real goal that I am willing to work for?
- Tangible: Does achieving this goal have value to me?

 Set a S.M.A.R.T. goal for the five priorities listed above.
Time with God (Example: Each day I will read two chapters of the Bible.)

1. _____

Time with Family (Example: Each week we will eat five meals together.)

2. _____

Time for Work (Example: This week I will complete the Smith proposal.)

3. _____

Time for Ministry (Example: I will call Joe and offer encouragement.)

4. _____

Professor Phitt says:

Exercise is an important stress-buster. Refer to page 72 in *Fit 4 Fitness Member Workbook* for ways to handle stress.

Time for Personal Renewal (Example: I will exercise three times a week.)

5. _____

MAINTAIN HEALTHY BOUNDARIES

Individuals who love God with all their minds maintain healthy boundaries with others. Boundaries are like a fence line around our personhood. Boundaries are limits that we set so that our energies are not exhausted. When our strength is constantly running near empty, we cannot be of service to God and others.

Our energies can be depleted when we allow the emotional problems of others to dominate our lives. Long-term involvement in emotionally demanding situations can lead to physical, mental, emotional, and spiritual exhaustion. We can allow the expectations of others to dictate our priorities, or we can allow God to set them. When others are in charge of our lives, we lose the balance that God will bring if we allow Him to be Lord. Learning to say a healthy "no" is not selfish; instead, it is treating our priorities as God-given guides to what He wants for us—not what others expect or want.

We move in a very fast-paced and demanding culture. We can't control all of life's variables. However, our Lord sees the big picture, knows every contributing variable, and wants us to take comfort in His sovereign rule. Live according to the priorities God has given you. Boundaries will help you live a balanced life.

If you have trouble setting and maintaining boundaries, begin the process with people you know and trust. Don't wait for permission or approval, and decide you can live without either if necessary. A firm resolve will help you stay the course. If you waver or give in, regroup and restart the process. A few false starts are typical and don't determine the final outcome.

 In weeks 3 and 4 we have studied the characteristics of those who love God with all their minds. List one meaningful idea for each characteristic.

Loving God with All My Mind

Seek godly wisdom: _____

Live as a thinking Christian: _____

Continue to learn and grow: _____

Have a healthy view of yourself: _____

Remember the importance of others: _____

Maintain healthy boundaries: _____

Week Five
Living with the Fall

The Bible gives us refreshing and candid descriptions of men and women who loved God. If we could gather them all together in a room to learn from them, they would share one additional attribute along with their love for the Lord. Each had a capacity to sin, which exerted a downward pull on their lives.

Paul confessed his own struggle in Romans 7:15. "I do not understand what I do. For what I want to do I do not do, but what I hate I do." Paul encountered instances where, even when he knew the right thing to do and wanted to do it, his efforts failed. He desired to be an obedient Christian, but the actual follow-through was missing. This dilemma lies at the heart of our struggle to live the Christian life. Fortunately, Paul did not end on a discouraging note! He went on to describe both his cry for help and God's answer in Christ. "What a wretched man I am! Who will rescue me from this body of death? Thanks be to God—through Jesus Christ our Lord!" (Rom. 7:24-25).

This week we will encounter the greatest obstacles that hinder us in our pursuit of loving God with all our minds. They include the results of the fall (our sin nature), temptations and deceptions, and the influences of the world. This focus will help us understand our own struggles and God's plan for renewal. Week 8 will show us how we can transform or change our thinking in a God-ward direction.

41

FALLEN!

This week's Verse To Know is an encouragement not to live as the Gentiles do in the "futility of their thinking." The Gentiles in Paul's day represented all non-Jews, but he meant all those non-Jews who had not trusted Christ for salvation. *Futile* means vain, fruitless, or ineffective. Because Paul encouraged us not to live in the "futility of our thinking," he made it clear that we have a choice in the matter. As Christians, we can choose to think productively and effectively.

 Take a moment to reflect on your thought patterns prior to becoming a Christian. What two or three topics most often occupied your mind?

_____

_____

Your thoughts were most likely about the things of this world: possessions, friendships, ambitions, and so on. Perhaps you were not filled with bad thoughts before you met Christ personally, but you were filled with earthly thoughts, thoughts that did not include or exalt God's kingdom and His purposes in this world. Without Christ, our thoughts are ineffective in producing lasting change in ourselves or others. They are futile!

Maybe your thoughts often went in a sinful direction. Your mind may have been filled with envy, lust, pride, hatred, fear, rebellion, or worry. In Romans 1:28 Paul spoke in terms of a "depraved mind" to describe the difficult position of those without Christ: "Furthermore, since they did not think it worthwhile to retain the knowledge of God, he gave them over to a depraved mind, to do what ought not to be done" (Rom. 1:28). "Depravity occurs as people choose to follow sinful desires rather than the knowledge of God revealed to them. … That depravity affects our thoughts, desires, will, and actions."[1]

 If you were to catalog your thoughts since becoming a Christian, would they be similar to previous thought patterns, or are your thoughts very different? Place an X on the line closest to the phrase that applies.

Very similar   Very different

The fallen state of the human race has left each individual with a fallen nature. When a person turns to Christ for salvation, that individual then has a capacity to follow Christ in obedience. Although the old nature remains, Christians have a new nature, as well. Our hope as Christians comes through yielding our minds to the control of the Spirit of God. The Spirit enables us to fellowship with God. Without Spirit-control, the new believer may function much like the unbeliever.

 Read Romans 8:6 in the margin. Underline the results of Spirit control.

> "The mind of sinful man is death, but the mind controlled by the Spirit is life and peace."
> —Romans 8:6

Abundant life in Christ and peace are valued qualities in the Christian life. I cannot overestimate the importance of yielding the control of our minds to the Spirit. "The way one thinks is intimately related to the way one lives, whether in Christ, in the Spirit and by faith, or alternatively in the flesh, in sin and in spiritual death."[2] The choice is clear: life or death. Moses told the Israelites, "I have set before you life and death, blessings and curses. Now choose life, so that you and your children may live and that you may love the Lord your God, listen to his voice, and hold fast to him. For the Lord is your life" (Deut. 30:19-20).

 Put an X on the line to indicate who most often controls your mind.

God's Spirit   Me (the flesh)

The fact that we are fallen has left us with both an old sinful nature and a renewed nature in Christ. Consequently, we still run the risk of being deceived in our thinking. In Galatians 6:7-8 Paul told the believers not to be deceived by their sinful natures because they would reap destruction.

TEMPTATIONS

As people with a sin nature, we experience temptations to sin. Temptation itself is not sin. Acting on the temptation or dwelling on the thought with desire or pleasure results in sin. Jesus said murder begins in the heart with anger (Matt. 5:21-22). Few words of encouragement can match Paul's promise to the Corinthians. Read 1 Corinthians 10:13 in the margin.

We should keep in mind several things when we are tempted.
1. Other people frequently face similar temptations. We should not focus on our uniqueness during times of temptation but realize that others have successfully resisted this temptation through the ages.
2. God will not allow us to be tempted beyond our capacity to endure. He knows our limitations. We can be assured that if God has permitted this temptation, He has not set us up to fail.
3. When we are tempted, He will provide a way out or past it. With any temptation we can trust in the Father's faithfulness to enable us and to give us the opportunity to respond positively.

Let's take a moment to apply God's promise to help us resist temptation to the areas of nutrition and fitness. If you are currently working the *Fit 4* plan, you probably have faced temptations to quit along the way. The discipline required to maintain proper nutrition may become a tedious exercise at times, and your capacity to endure may grow thin. Your intentions to keep up a balanced fitness plan may diminish with bad weather or schedule changes.

Cheer up! Your heavenly Father loves you and wants to help. We often forget that He is our resource and help in time of trouble (Ps. 46:1). However, we must remember to call on Him. Ask for God's help in resisting temptation.

"No temptation has seized you except what is common to man. And God is faithful; he will not let you be tempted beyond what you can bear. But when you are tempted, he will also provide a way out so that you can stand up under it."
—1 Corinthians 10:13

UPREACH
Write Psalm 46:1 on a card or slip of paper. Keep it with you and read it during times of temptation.

Professor Phitt says:

Use the daily pages in your *Accountability Journal* to record food and exercise choices. This discipline will help you make "one wise choice at a time," our *Fit 4* theme.

"Everyone has heard about your obedience, so I am full of joy over you; but I want you to be wise about what is good, and innocent about what is evil. The God of peace will soon crush Satan under your feet. The grace of our Lord Jesus be with you."
—Romans 16:19-20

Put a check by the areas of greatest temptation for you. (You will find the *Fit 4* studies on nutrition and fitness helpful.)

NUTRITION
- ❑ High intake of sweets or carbs
- ❑ Desire to return to past patterns of poor nutrition
- ❑ Poor planning of meals/snacks
- ❑ Eating fast food on a regular basis

FITNESS
- ❑ Failure to make time for exercise
- ❑ Desire to return to past patterns of non-exercise
- ❑ Not getting enough rest

At this point I want to spend a moment talking about Satan's tactics. This is an important area for us to grasp as Christians. In writing about the devil, Paul emphasized three key points: Our part is to be obedient, God's part is to crush Satan, and the grace of the Lord Jesus made it all possible. Jesus paid the price so that we are saved by grace, not works. Read Romans 16:19-20 in the margin.

Remind yourself often of these three points: I can and must obey because through the grace of Jesus, Satan is a defeated enemy. When Paul wrote about the enemy, he sought to maintain a focus on Jesus Christ. When we are commanded to "put on the full armor of God" (Eph. 6:11), we are first told to "be strong in the Lord and in his mighty power" (Eph. 6:10). Every spiritual battle we will ever face will be fought and won by Jesus Christ, as we place our faith in Him. We have to make decisions to live in a disciplined manner, but if we trust Him, He will help us to achieve our goals.

Paul understood that our struggle was not against men and women, but against the spiritual forces that are set against us. "Our struggle is not against flesh and blood, but against the rulers, against the authorities, against the powers of this dark world and against the spiritual forces of evil in the heavenly realms" (Eph. 6:12).

Read Ephesians 6:10-18. Evaluate the state of your spiritual armor. How are you currently employing each of the following elements of the full armor of God?

1. The belt of truth buckled around your waist
Am I honest with God, myself, and others?
- ❑ Yes
- ❑ Sometimes
- ❑ No

2. The breastplate of righteousness
Am I protected by cultivating the righteousness of Christ?
- ❑ Yes
- ❑ Sometimes
- ❑ No

3. **Your feet fitted with the readiness that comes from the gospel of peace**

   Am I standing firm and at peace through the truth of the gospel of Jesus Christ?

   ❑ Yes   ❑ Sometimes   ❑ No

4. **The shield of faith**

   When Satan attempts to deceive, do I deflect his attacks?

   ❑ Yes   ❑ Sometimes   ❑ No

5. **The helmet of salvation**

   Is my head/mind protected by the knowledge of my salvation in Christ?

   ❑ Yes   ❑ Sometimes   ❑ No

6. **The sword of the Spirit that is the Word of God**

   Do I counter Satan's lies by the truth in God's Word?

   ❑ Yes   ❑ Sometimes   ❑ No

7. **Praying in the Spirit on all occasions with all kinds of prayers and requests**

   With my mind controlled by the Spirit of God, do I pray about my concerns and the concerns of others?

   ❑ Yes   ❑ Sometimes   ❑ No

WORLDLY INFLUENCES

We have discussed two of the major obstacles we face in loving God with all our minds: our fallen natures and the problem of temptation. The third major obstacle consists of the influences of the world around us. When I speak of the world, I don't mean all the people of the world whom God loves and for whom Jesus died. I mean the world as a persuasion for evil, "the powers of this dark world" (see Eph. 6:12)—the evil spiritual rulers and authorities that are behind the corruption we see in the world around us.

In week 3 we learned that a Christian worldview consists of the creation, the fall of mankind, and the redemption found through faith in Christ. As Christians we must be realistic in our understanding of the world around us. It is fallen. God does not want us to retreat to a cabin in the mountains for the sole purpose of escaping the world; otherwise, we could not influence it.

However, He does want us to be aware of the negative influences that the world can have on us. We are bombarded each day by images from the media that give us a false standard of beauty, significance, and success. If we are not fully alert to this deception, we will have our ideas concerning healthy standards and priorities influenced in a negative direction.

OUTREACH

Jesus said we are to be in the world yet not of the world (John 17:14).
How do you try to influence the world?

Do you influence it more than it influences you? (circle)

yes   no

Three key ideas from this passage enable us to have success against the three negative influences we have been discussing.

When Paul wrote his second letter to Timothy, he encouraged him to make a firm response to the negative influences of his sinful nature, temptations, and the world. "Flee the evil desires of youth, and pursue righteousness, faith, love and peace, along with those who call on the Lord out of a pure heart" (2:22). Three key ideas from this passage enable us to have success against the three negative influences we have been discussing.

First, we must *flee* (run away) from the evil desires or urges that could lead to sin. When we choose to flee these desires, we will decline to go certain places, refuse to view ungodly images, and resist unhealthy relationships with people. We cannot be "innocent about what is evil" (Rom. 16:19) if we constantly expose ourselves to it. **Second,** we need to *pursue* the things that make for spiritual growth: righteousness, faith, love, and peace. The fact that you are completing this study indicates your desire to grow as a Christian. **Third,** we need to *be accountable* to healthy Christians. Ask others to pray for you in your specific areas of temptation.

The three key ideas from 2 Timothy 2:22 can play an important role in your attempts to live in a godly manner. They can help you to make a firm response to the negative influences discussed in this chapter. Charles Ryrie described these three ways to win over temptation as follows: "Temptation is to be avoided by fleeing what hinders, by following what helps, and by seeking the company of spiritual people."[3]

 Take a moment to evaluate your life in view of 2 Timothy 2:22.
1. **Personal limits:** What sins do I need to *flee*?

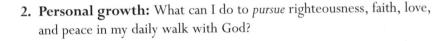

2. **Personal growth:** What can I do to *pursue* righteousness, faith, love, and peace in my daily walk with God?

Has your study group developed an accountability relationship? Are there persons in your group in whom you feel you could confide? Could you be a reliable accountability partner for someone else?

3. **Be accountable to healthy Christians:** To whom can I be accountable (confide in) concerning the ups and downs of my life?

———————

[1]*Disciple's Study Bible* (Nashville: Holman Bible Publishers, 1988), 1418.

[2]J. Goetzmann, "Mind," *The New International Dictionary Of New Testament Theology*, vol. 2, ed. Colin Brown (Grand Rapids, MI: Zondervan Publishing House, 1986), 617.

[3]Charles C. Ryrie, *The Ryrie Study Bible* (Chicago: Moody Press, 1978), 1826.

Week Six
Living with the Past

Those who worked with Michael or knew him in a casual way considered him to be a great success. His relaxed mannerisms, good looks, and intelligence had served him well in the business world. When Michael and his family sat together in church on Sundays, they looked like the American dream.

However, in my office Michael sat with a dejected look on his face. As he slowly began to express his troubled thoughts, Michael recounted situation after situation in which he felt inadequate or—in his words—defective. His wife encouraged him when he felt down. She reminded him of his accomplishments, loving family, and good character. Yet, at age 35, he still felt that his efforts fell short of an acceptable standard. He knew his outlook was distorted, but he couldn't figure out exactly why.

Spiritually, Michael knew and loved the Lord. We talked about his relationship with Christ and his understanding of forgiveness and growth. Relationally, Michael spoke affectionately of his wife and clearly thought the world of her. He was a good father and loved his children deeply. But when we came to a discussion of his father, there was a long pause. He was slow to speak at first but gradually revealed a history of shortcomings, disappointments, and even fear. His father had demanded perfection. He had owned a car dealership in which Michael had worked from a young age. When Michael was 10, he was expected to keep each car on the lot shining, but his work rarely passed inspection. In high school he had to clean the floors where the mechanics had worked all day. His father inspected the work—the standard was perfection, and that was all Michael ever knew.

Finally, at age 18, Michael left home, never to return. His ability to work hard and long served him well as he put himself through college. Yet, while he hated his father, he emulated his standard of perfection. This drive served him well for a time, until he began to predominantly focus on his own shortcomings.

Some of those who sat near Michael each Sunday morning in church might have been very surprised to hear his feelings of inadequacy. When people such as

UPREACH

Read what God said about Himself in Exodus 34:6-7. Is this description your image of God? Why or why not?

Michael are reared with unrealistic standards and distortions of human perfection, they often form unrealistic images of who they should be as persons and what they should be able to accomplish.

Many who work through this study will have had childhoods that were very different from Michael's. Others may have had equally troubling home situations, such as alcohol abuse, painful divorces, or even physical or mental abuse that God never intended for any child. We want to discover the effects of some of these situations. For those who had a very positive experience, you can use this week's study as a means of further understanding others. Individuals you know may have faced and overcome some very negative life circumstances.

In week 2 we examined Paul's discourse with Greek philosophers in the marketplace of Athens. He described God as the One who had "made the world and everything in it" (Acts 17:24). In this week's verse, we are told that we are God's offspring; therefore, we shouldn't try to remake God in an image we fashion. When people are left to their own imaginations, they form false images of God. A false image of God lends itself to a false image of mankind.

Think of an example of this premise: A false idea of God leads to a false idea about people. Write it below.

_____

_____

_____

Some who see God as angry and judgmental will assume that their peers feel the same way about them. If a person views God as disinterested in His universe, he or she may interpret others' actions as showing indifference. A realistic view of God helps us to view ourselves and others more realistically. This change of viewpoint is especially important if you grew up with distorted images of reality.

PARENTAL INFLUENCE

Recall from week 2 that God gives parents a wonderful opportunity to influence their children (see pp. 21-23). When Paul wrote to the church at Colosse, he gave some very helpful instructions to guide family relationships. Each family member had his or her own particular set of roles and responsibilities to others in the family (see Col. 3:18-21). Paul had similar instructions for the church at Ephesus and encouraged fathers in this way: "Fathers, do not exasperate your children; instead, bring them up in the training and instruction of the Lord" (Eph. 6:4).

Training and instructing children requires a great deal of time. Moses spoke to this important role of teaching God's commandments. "Impress them on your children. Talk about them when you sit at home and when you walk along the road, when you lie down and when you get up" (Deut. 6:7).

Children have a limited capacity to understand life. They are dependent on their parents for physical, emotional, and spiritual growth. What we say makes a profound impression on our children. The word *teach* is in an intensive Hebrew verb form and becomes "teach diligently," or "impress these words on them!" The responsibility of parents extends from sunup to sundown, and both inside and outside of the house.

From Michael's story on page 47, we learned that Michael's father instructed him; but, due to harsh, unrealistic standards, Michael ultimately became discouraged and embittered—the very thing that Paul encouraged fathers to avoid.

 Take a moment to consider what we just discussed. Paul gave three results of unhealthy parenting. To what extent were these true in your development through childhood? Place an X on the line that most closely resembles your experience.

1. I became bitter (Col. 3:21).

Never   Frequently

2. I grew discouraged (Col. 3:21).

Never   Frequently

3. I was frustrated—angered, enraged, inflamed (Eph. 6:4).

Never   Frequently

This exercise is not meant to blame our parents for our shortcomings. Part of emotional maturity is learning to accept responsibility for our thoughts, feelings, and actions. No one makes us respond in a certain way. However, if you have been bent in a certain direction by childhood experiences, you will have to make the choice to reprogram, to enter new data into your internal computer (review pp. 17-18).

THE EFFECTS OF PARENTAL INFLUENCE

Look at the chart on the following page. It does not cover every problem area, but it does give a quick picture of how parenting styles can affect young children. It also demonstrates how those effects continue into adult life.

For example, if you often find yourself experiencing shame over a mistake or misjudgment, perhaps you heard emotionally abusive words from your parents or significant others: "You're an idiot. You never get anything right." A simple frown from a coworker or supervisor can bring back those feelings of unworthiness.

 Circle words or phrases in the right column of the chart on page 50 which represent feelings or actions that are common for you.

OUTREACH

If you are a parent, to what extent does your parenting model that of your parents?

dissimilar   very similar

What effects do you expect your parenting model will have on your children?

NEGATIVE PARENTAL INFLUENCES

Action of Parent	Childhood Problems	Future Adult Problems
Physical Abuse	Pain Fear Anger	Creates angry adults May repeat abuse on spouse and children

Sexual Abuse	Normal childhood
	  development is
	  interrupted
		Decreases trust
		Meets problems with
		  escape (daydreams,
		  avoidance)

Emotional Abuse	Damaged confidence	Lowered self-esteem Overreactions to perceived humiliations

Alcohol/Drugs	Adoption of specific roles
	  example: defender of
	  mother or sibling
	Energy spent protecting
	  the alcoholic
		Rigid: heightened desire
		  for order in life
		Greater chance of
		  alcohol/drug abuse

Divorce	Child learns that marriage
	  may be temporary
	Small Children—unmet
	  needs for security
	Teens—possibility of self-
	  destructive behaviors
		Insecurity
		Marriage may be
		  temporary
		Fears of rejection or
		  abandonment

Focus on Rules
(Boundaries are
too firm)
	Produces inadequacy	Overly self-controlled
		(Acceptance comes
		  through a perfect
		  performance)
		Critical of others—
		  especially spouse/
		  children

Focus on Freedom
(Boundaries
do not exist)
	Too many experiences
	  too soon
	Potential for a
	  wild childhood
		Lack of self-control
		  and accountability
		  to others
		Frustrates spouse/children
		  (they feel neglected)

Perhaps the material you just read brings up some painful memories, thoughts, or feelings for you or someone close to you. If so, think about the fact that Jesus loved you as a child and wanted God's best for you. He loves you still and is committed to your healing of these painful feelings. Read Mark 10:13-16. Pray this prayer along with me:

Lord, thank You that You have always loved me, and You love me today. I confess that I do not fully understand many things about You or even about myself. But I thank You that You know me. I give myself and all of my experiences to You. If anything in my past hinders me from loving You with all of my heart, soul, mind, and strength, reveal it to me and help me to be an overcomer in Christ. Amen.

UNREALISTIC THINKING

One of the key points to understanding the unresolved problems of childhood is to realize that children tend to view their circumstances as normal. This fact is generally true throughout the early stages of development. Even when family dynamics and relational patterns are hurtful, children do not view their situation as abnormal. The family is a child's first view of society; it is the child's world.

When children must shape their behavior to fit the unrealistic needs and expectations of others, their lives are being set on a difficult course. Children have a deep need for their parents' love. Consequently, if their parents are healthy, well-balanced individuals who love God and others, children will emulate their characteristics. But if their parents are not healthy and are not primarily motivated by love (both of God and others), children will then be drawn to practice unhealthy characteristics. Children have an innate tendency to want to please their parents.

This week opened with Michael's story. His father was unrealistic in his expectations. Michael labored under those demands for 18 years until they were ingrained in his personality. Remember that in week 2 we defined personality as inner characteristics that produce outer actions. Michael was molded and shaped in such a way that he was unbalanced. Between the extremes of *doing a good job* and *I'm human and I have limitations,* Michael became much too perfectionistic in outlook and tended to put himself down when he could not match his expectations (which were often not God's expectations for him).

Each assumption that you make affects your thoughts. These thoughts form the basis for how you view God, yourself, and the world around you. Each unrealistic assumption will negatively influence your actions and feelings. In turn, realistic assumptions have the effect of positively influencing your actions and feelings. Although we might laugh at the false assumption that people can fly, we are not so quick to pick up on the equally false assumption that all boys should be athletic and all girls beauty queens.

So, how do you know what is realistic and what is not? How do you assess truth from error? When children are raised in the "training and instruction of the Lord" (Eph. 6:4), they are introduced to the standard for truth: God and His Word. Jesus

"People were bringing little children to Jesus to have him touch them, but the disciples rebuked them. When Jesus saw this, he was indignant. He said to them, 'Let the little children come to me, and do not hinder them, for the kingdom of God belongs to such as these. I tell you the truth, anyone who will not receive the kingdom of God like a little child will never enter it.' And he took the children in his arms, put his hands on them and blessed them."
—Mark 10:13-16

INREACH

List an unrealistic assumption you have made about yourself in the past. Then list the more realistic image that has replaced it.

Professor Phitt

Did you know that exercise has been shown to be a mood elevator? If you often find yourself dealing with the blues, take a brisk walk, climb stairs, or perform flexibility exercises *(see **Fit 4** Fitness Members Workbook, p. 57).*

" 'Forget the former things;
   do not dwell on the past.
See, I am doing a new thing!
   Now it springs up; do you
   not perceive it?
I am making a way in
   the desert
   and streams in the
   wasteland.' "
   —Isaiah 43:18-19

said, " 'I am … the truth' " (John 14:6). If you experienced distortions in your reality growing up, ground yourself in God's truth. Study His Word. Associate with godly people. Continue to participate in discipleship studies such as this.

🏃 I have listed a set of assumptions people hold. Put a check by the messages that you give yourself:

❏ Everything I do should please others, or my work is somehow flawed.
❏ If I don't perform positively at everything I do, then something is wrong with me.
❏ God expects me to finish at the top of my class; second place is last place.
❏ When I have set plans for myself, they should proceed just as planned.
❏ What happened to me in the past has determined my course in life; I can't change the outcome now.
❏ If I let people see the real me—my thoughts, ideas, and dreams— they would not like me.
❏ Every minute of the day needs to be accounted for and productive.
❏ I should not need the help of others to be happy and successful.
❏ If others are angry or discouraged, it is probably my fault.
❏ If people around me are unhappy, it is my responsibility to make them happy.
❏ To show emotions is sinful. I must never be angry at anything or anyone.
❏ When I awake in the morning, I should always feel energetic and ready to take on the day.

The more messages that you checked above, the more likely you are to be hindering yourself in loving God with all of your mind. You may have found parts of these assumptions to be true in certain contexts, but as rules to live by, they tend to leave a person feeling anxious, inadequate, and often angry.

OVERCOMING PAST EXPERIENCES

In these past two weeks we have examined the obstacles to loving God with all our minds. In weeks 7-9 we will discuss the change process, as we seek to think about ourselves and others in a realistic manner. For now, be assured that you are not stuck with unrealistic assumptions and their accompanying effects. Michael's story had a happy ending, and yours can also. Read the words of Isaiah in the margin.

🏃 Are you forgetting the former things and refusing to dwell on the past? (circle)   yes   no

If so, what new thing is God doing in your life to make a way through

your desert?_____

Renewing Your Mind

What's on your mind right now? What subject most occupies your thoughts? *Why* are you thinking about it? *How* are you thinking about it? That is, what type of thoughts does this subject tend to evoke? Are you attempting to solve a problem, nurse a wound, plan a schedule, or escape from a task? Are your thoughts mostly positive or negative?

In weeks 3-4 we explored mental fitness and the question, *What are the characteristics or marks of believers who love the Lord with all their minds?* Weeks 5-6 centered our attention on the things that may hinder us in our pursuit of a healthy mind. The better we understand these obstacles, the better able we will be to utilize God's plan for growth and renewal. This week we want to begin answering the question, *How can we transform, or change our thinking in a God-ward direction?* All this helps us arrive at the goal for this study: to love the Lord with all our minds!

Four years ago, Brian and Gail came to a conclusion that changed the course of their lives. Both of them had grown up in strong Christian homes where the Bible was believed, God was real, and attending church was an important part of the week. They met in college and were quickly attracted to each other. They married following graduation and began a happy life together. Yet as time went on, almost without realizing what was happening, they slowly began to move away from their earlier foundations. They still prayed before meals and attended church, but it became apparent that something was lacking. Brian became less interested in talking (Gail called it *communication*). Gail seemed frequently irritable, and Brian found her sharp-edged comments difficult to take.

On a rainy Sunday morning in October, neither smiled as the family rode to church. Each silently prayed for help and—thankfully—each received an answer that day. The pastor preached a simple message on change from Romans 12:2, and it led to recommitment and a fresh desire to grow. Although they had both been Christians since childhood, they had not fully grasped that they needed to make daily choices for personal change.

The changes that Brian and Gail have made in the last four years did not occur overnight. But Brian says that Gail has gradually taken on a new gentleness, and Gail finds Brian much more willing to listen and to share his life with her.

THE SIGNIFICANCE OF THE MIND

In week 1 of our study I pointed you to the riveting words of A. W. Tozer, "Were we able to extract from any man a complete answer to the question, 'What comes into your mind when you think about God?' We might predict with certainty the spiritual future of that man."[1] If we perceive God as a tyrant, our motivation level for getting to know Him better will be low.

The use of our minds and how we think are central ideas in Paul's letter to the Romans. Let's trace some of the concepts from Romans that we have highlighted throughout this study. In essence, we have been moving toward the idea of transforming a depraved mind into one that is controlled by God's Spirit.

The Depraved Mind

In Romans 1:28 Paul spoke in terms of a "depraved mind" to describe the broken position of those without Christ. "Furthermore, since they did not think it worthwhile to retain the knowledge of God, he gave them over to a depraved mind, to do what ought not to be done."

Paul warned his young pastor-friend Timothy about those with a depraved mind in 2 Timothy 3:1-9. Read these verses in your Bible. Note the characteristics of people with depraved minds.

List some expected consequences of allowing our minds to be taken over by negative or sinful thinking.

_____

_____

_____

After his conversion, Paul confessed to his own struggle in Romans 7:15. "I do not understand what I do. For what I want to do I do not do, but what I hate I do." Paul said that even when he knew the right thing to do, and even wanted to do it, his efforts at times failed. The desire to be an obedient Christian was there, but the actual follow-through was not. This dilemma is at the heart of Christian living.

The Mind Yielded to God's Spirit

The fallen state of the human race has left each individual with a fallen nature. When a person turns to Christ for salvation, that individual has a capacity to follow Christ in obedience. However, the old nature remains. Our hope as Christians comes through yielding our minds to the control of the Spirit of God.

"The mind of sinful man is death, but the mind controlled by the Spirit is life and peace."
—Romans 8:6

Yielding control of our minds to the Spirit is essential because the Spirit enables us to walk with God. The way we think is essentially related to the way we live. We have no such thing as neutral thinking. We generally have our minds set on something or someone. This is one of the central concerns of the apostle Paul in our study. In fact, we read in Romans 8:5 that "Those who live according to the sinful nature have their minds set on what that nature desires; but those who live in accordance with the Spirit have their minds set on what the Spirit desires."

Paul wrote that we can make a choice about how to "set" or direct our thoughts. Our minds have a tremendous influence on the direction of our lives. We can choose to change.

THE TRANSFORMED MIND

Negative thoughts and attitudes can be transformed as we learn to change our thinking. We will focus on the important process of being transformed by the renewing of our mind this week, while learning to set our thoughts on things above in next week's study.

Paul gives us three actions necessary to transforming a depraved mind into one that is controlled by God's Spirit. Reread our Verse to Know for this week—Romans 12:2—on page 65. Can you say it from memory?

1. Offer your bodies as living sacrifices. Transformation begins as we offer our bodies to God. Paul urged us to reflect on God's mercy that was described in the previous 11 chapters of the Book of Romans. God offers us eternal life in Christ and the joy of living in fellowship with Him. Offering all of ourselves to God is at the heart of the *Fit 4* continuing studies series. We want to grow in loving the Lord our God with all our heart, soul, mind, and strength (Mark 12:30).

In the Old Testament sacrificial system, only animals without defect were acceptable for sacrifice. When we offer our bodies (which includes our minds) to God, He wants a pure and blameless offering. That requires us to take care of our bodies as a good steward of the vessels He has entrusted to us. Does this mean you have to be perfect? No, but it does mean that you desire holiness.

2. Be transformed by the renewing of your mind. We have a choice in life to become increasingly more like the world around us or to redirect our minds to God by yielding to the control of His Spirit. You will recall that when Paul used the word *world* in this context, he meant the world as a persuasion for evil, "the powers of this dark world" (Eph. 6:12).

Evil spiritual rulers and authorities promote the corruption that we see in the world around us, so the choice should not be a hard one. We either turn our minds to the world, ruled by darkness and evil, or to Christ and the control of His Spirit, which offers life and peace (Rom. 8:6). Renewal is the process of renovation, replacement, and replenishment. Some old things must go; new ways of living must be added. Replenishment comes from the Spirit's constant infilling.

Professor Phitt asks:
In what ways are you seeking to present your body as a living sacrifice to God in the way you

eat? _____

sleep? _____

exercise? _____

manage stress? _____

UPREACH

List some good gifts
from God.

Tell Him how grateful you are
for His loving provision.

3. Experience the joy of living out God's will. Our decision to offer ourselves to God in order to make personal changes has a very positive result. We are able to test out, or prove for ourselves the good, pleasing, and perfect will of God. Just as David said, "Taste and see that the Lord is good; blessed is the man who takes refuge in him" (Ps. 34:8).

When you and I choose to yield our minds to the control of God's Spirit, to take refuge in Him, we discover by our own experience that He is good. Jesus said that if earthly fathers know how to give good gifts to their children, how much more does your heavenly Father want to give good gifts to those who ask Him (Matt. 7:11). Let's take a moment to pray.

> *Dear Father, I thank You for Your kindness and mercy in sending Your Son to die for me. I gladly offer my body to You as a living sacrifice. Please let me know when I am conforming myself to the world. I want to yield my mind to the control of Your Spirit and to be changed. I want to experience the joy of living out Your will day by day. Thank You for Your mercy and love. Amen.*

The genuine mark of Christians is that they seek to be God-centered rather than self-centered. Getting out of ourselves gets us in touch with those around us. Paul continued his message to the Christians at Rome, encouraging them to be characterized by an attitude of humility toward one another. He wanted them to live with each other in a humble and unassuming manner (Rom 12:16, NASB).

THE CHANGE PROCESS

A model for change was introduced in the *Fit 4 Nutrition Member Workbook.*[2] We want to examine the model in view of today's verse in Romans 12:2. The model has four stages:

> Develop Awareness
> Gain Knowledge
> Take Action
> Experience Change

Stage 1: Develop Awareness

Change often begins when God suggests a specific direction to follow. For Brian and Gail it occurred on that Sunday morning in October. They both knew they needed help, they silently prayed, and God answered.

🏃 As you have studied this book, has God made you aware of areas in your life that need to be changed? List the major areas or ideas God has brought to your mind.

_____

_____

When God creates a new awareness in us, it often produces a situation that challenges ideas or actions we have long held dear. The most natural response to this first stage is to reject that new information in an attempt to erase the awareness that God has given us.

 Read the statements below. God may want to make you aware of some of them to effect change in your life. Check the ones that apply to you.

❑ I am too defensive.
❑ My priorities are confused.
❑ I need to rest more.
❑ I need more time alone with God.
❑ I need more exercise.
❑ I need better nutrition.

❑ I am too busy.
❑ I may need medical help.
❑ I get angry too easily.
❑ I appear to be friends with many people, yet know none of them well.
❑ I am not a lifelong learner.

When God brings about a new awareness in your life, remember that:
1. It may take you out of your comfort zone.
2. It may take time to develop.
3. You may need to ask God to confirm that the change initiative is from Him.
4. You may deny or reject the truth.

Stage 2: Gain Knowledge

The process of gaining knowledge requires us to collect information through a variety of sources, including books, articles, online information, and other people.

 In the areas where God has brought to your mind the need for change, what actions have you taken to collect helpful information?

❑ read a book or magazine article
❑ read my Bible and other study helps
❑ consulted informed persons

❑ searched the Internet
❑ prayed about it
❑ haven't taken any

Ask your group and group leader for help as you seek understanding.

When a person fully accepts his new awareness from God as *true* and has gained knowledge from a variety of sources, he has reached the stage of understanding. The struggle is completed as the person says, *Yes, I accept the fact that God has revealed this to me.* Knowledge may be illustrated by the word *Oh!* Understanding, on the other hand, is closer to an experience of *Aha! I get it!*

Knowledge   Understanding

INREACH

Your *Accountability Journal* contains daily pages that help you assess your need for change. Continue to use this process of daily review or if you have not used it in the past, begin today.

Stage 3: Take Action

Next comes the question, *What do I do now? I understand what God has revealed to me and I accept it, but how do I implement what I have learned?* This stage finds us taking the first steps of a new behavior. We don't need to have complete awareness, knowledge, and understanding to begin to act. God wants us to use and respond to the new insights that He gives us immediately. In fact, our understanding grows as we put it into practice. This is God's apprenticeship program—living out the truth of His Word in daily life.

This stage is similar to learning to walk. We are beginning to try out a new behavior. Some degree of failure is particularly likely at the beginning when we attempt to perform a task that we have never done before. How many toddlers begin walking and never take a tumble? As a father, I have been privileged to run alongside the bikes of my children, holding tightly to the seat as they tried to balance this new two-wheeled experience. My children never took off successfully the first time, precisely because it was a new behavior, a new skill. I think God works with us in the same way. We might think that He expects a perfect first attempt, but He is our Father and looks for effort on our part, not perfection.

Any change works the same way. The first few attempts are awkward and rarely successful. We fall back into the same old patterns and have to begin again. The point is that by God's grace we are trying new ways to live our lives.

 What new actions can you take now to help deal with the areas of change that you noted? List two of these actions below and the date you put the behavior into practice. An example is found in the margin.

Area of Change	Action	Date
_____	_____	_____
_____	_____	_____
_____	_____	_____

Stage 4: Experience Change

This is the final stage of the change process—the culmination of the three previous stages. At this point we are living more of our lives with the new behavior or attitude in place than without it. For example, if a person believed God would have him give up a wounded spirit toward another Christian, change would involve consistently replacing negative thoughts about that individual with positive ones. The new thought pattern would be present most of the time.

How does this process happen? First, we must become aware of our thoughts. Did you know that you have to think about your thoughts? If you struggle with negative thoughts such as anxiety, fear, anger, criticism, or revenge, you must identify these thoughts as contrary to God's will for your life. You can know for sure if your

Example
Area of Change:
I need to stop worrying about things I cannot control.

Action: When worrying thoughts come into my mind, I will replace them by quoting Matthew 6:25.

Date: October 15

thoughts are pleasing to God through Bible study, prayer, church participation, Christian friendships, and the conviction of the Holy Spirit. Thoughts that do not please God produce deadly consequences (Rom. 8:6). Then, we must "take captive" those thoughts that displease God. Read 2 Corinthians 10:5.

We consciously choose to replace the unwholesome thoughts with wholesome thoughts. Perhaps you are thinking, *I've tried not to dwell on a certain problem or relationship, but I have not been successful in replacing those thoughts.*

Check the statements that you consider true for you.
- ❏ I have the choice as to what I think about.
- ❏ I can consciously choose to think positive, uplifting thoughts.
- ❏ When I find myself thinking negative or unhelpful thoughts, I can quickly intercept these thoughts, ask forgiveness, and move on.
- ❏ If I continue old thought patterns as a consistent practice, I am not truly committed to change.

I do not wish to be harsh or judging, but in my counseling experience I find that unsuccessful attempts at changing thought patterns result from an unwillingness to change them. We enjoy our misery or woundedness or lustfulness or pride more than we desire godliness. Unless our motivation is to please God, our attempts at thought-control will have limited success. The Holy Spirit empowers our change process when we are truly repentant and wanting His control.

A MODEL FOR CHANGE FROM ROMANS

The following chart summarizes our goal of a renewed mind in Romans 12:2.

Develop Awareness	We have a sin nature that pulls us toward ungodliness. The role of the Holy Spirit is to convict us of sin. He may use Scripture, events, or other means.
Gain Knowledge	Even as Christians, the desire to do the right thing is not consistent with what we know to be right (Rom. 7:15). Our hope comes through yielding our minds to the control of the Holy Spirit (Rom. 8:5-6). Bible study, worship, and prayer guide this process.
Take Action	In Romans 12:1-2, Paul urged us to offer our bodies (which includes our minds) to God as a living sacrifice. Rather than being conformed, or directed toward the world, we are to be renewed by yielding the control of our minds to God's Spirit.
Experience Change	The transformation takes place as we become conscious of our thoughts and direct them in wholesome ways. We experience renewed minds and the joy of daily living out God's will for us.

"We demolish arguments and every pretension that sets itself up against the knowledge of God, and we take captive every thought to make it obedient to Christ."
—2 Corinthians 10:5

OUTREACH
Spending most of your time with negative or ungodly friends will not encourage your growth toward godliness. Cultivate friendships that lead you to wholesome thoughts and activities.

Change does not mean perfection. It means experiencing more of the new behavior than the old. God offers hope by providing us with a strategy that will lead to lasting change.

 Where are you in reaching your goal for a renewed mind? (Review p.13.) Place a check at the stage where you find yourself at this point in time.

Developing Awareness	Growing in Knowledge and Understanding	Taking Action	Experiencing Change

In the margin, explain why you are at the point where you placed the check. What do you need to do to continue the change process?

This week's Verse to Know is especially helpful in loving God with all of your mind. Write it from memory.

_____

_____

_____

_____

[1]A. W. Tozer, *The Knowledge of the Holy* (San Francisco, CA: Harper & Row Publishers, 1961), 1.

[2]Adapted from *Fit 4 Nutrition Member Workbook* (Nashville, TN: LifeWay Press, 2000), 23-27 and *Strength for the Journey: A Biblical Perspective on Discouragement and Depression* (Nashville, TN: LifeWay Press, 1999).

Setting Your Mind on Things Above

Jessica had been a Christian for five years when she came to our house to talk with me and my wife Ginny. Jessica said that while others seemed able to enjoy themselves, for some reason it was hard for her. She described her life as more of an existence than a joy. To the best of her ability she was seeking to live as a Christian but felt more hemmed-in than free. With evident frustration she asked, "If Jesus set me free, why do I feel burdened with life?"

Jessica's question demanded a helpful answer, but we needed more information. In further conversations, it became clear that she was focusing too much on what a Christian should not do rather than on what one should do. This self-focus had resulted in a lot of wary introspection instead of a healthy focus on Christ. Her inward focus had made it difficult to enjoy social settings because she continually judged her actions and attitudes. This behavior is not wrong—we do need to examine ourselves before God—but it can become unbalanced. Part of yielding our minds to the control of God's Spirit is allowing God to be our judge, rather than for us to constantly judge ourselves.

Paul provided us with the proper balance when he encouraged us in this week's Verses to Know to set our minds on things above. This week we want to explore what God enables us to see as we look upward at Him.

Our emphasis last week and again this week is change: *What process has God given to transform our thinking?* The answer to this question has two parts. First, as Brian and Gail learned last week, we need to make daily choices for personal change. We begin by offering ourselves to God and conforming ourselves to God's thinking rather than to the mindset of the world. Second, as we will discover in this week's study, we choose to set our minds on things above. Our focus remains on God.

SET YOUR THOUGHTS UPWARD

When we focus our attention upward, we see our past, present, and future centered in Christ. Paul described what our hearts recognize as we look at Jesus seated at the right hand of God.

> "Set your minds on things above, not on earthly things. For you died, and your life is now hidden with Christ in God."
> —Colossians 3:2-3

In your Bible read Colossians 3:1-4. Underline all the occurrences of the words *you* and *your*. Personalize this passage. Replace these words with your own name when you see them in this passage.

Since God chose to raise us up with Christ, He made it possible for us to look up. Let's review the significance of our past, present, and future in Jesus Christ.

1. In the Past

In the past we symbolically died and have been raised to a new life (Col. 3:3). People with an upward focus are aware that their past is behind them. This realization is especially important as we seek to understand the obstacles to loving God with all our minds.

- We still have a sin nature.
- We are continually being tempted.
- We are influenced by the world.

These obstacles, identified in week 5, are overcome to the extent that we grow in our recognition of our death to our old way of life. Paul developed this point in Romans 6:8-11. Read it in the margin.

 Imagine you are teaching a Sunday School class of 4th graders (approximately 9-10 years old). One of them with a puzzled look asks, "what does it mean to have died with Christ?" How would you answer the question?

_____

_____

The payment for sin is death (Rom. 6:23). We have been spared death—separation from God—and given eternal life through Jesus' payment for our sins. His victory over sin and death gives us the ability to "die" to sin and live a new life.

2. In the Present

We understand baptism by immersion as a picture that we died and were raised with Christ. Today our life is hidden with Christ in God (Col. 3:3). The storms that some of us endured at the hands of others growing up may seem as if they can never be stilled, but as we picture ourselves "hidden in Christ," storms begin to calm and a sense of safety grows. We do not expect instant healing. While the new birth comes in an instant, growth is a change process. Allow God the period of time that He decides to use for healing. He proclaimed, "I am the Lord, who heals you" (Ex. 15:26).

 What do you think Paul meant when he said that "your life is hidden with Christ in God" (Col. 3:3)? On the next page, place a check by one or more responses.

"Now if we died with Christ, we believe that we will also live with him. For we know that since Christ was raised from the dead, he cannot die again; death no longer has mastery over him. The death he died, he died to sin once for all; but the life he lives, he lives to God. In the same way, count yourselves dead to sin but alive to God in Christ Jesus."
—Romans 6:8-11

❑ I am hidden from view.
❑ No one sees what I will one day be.
❑ I am in a place of safety: secure and protected.

Is God your refuge in times of trouble (Ps. 46:1)? If not, He wants to be your source of security, your safety net. His protection offers you the chance to grow in Christlikeness so that you may become all that He intended for you.

3. In the Future

In the future we know that Christ will appear in glory at His second coming. When we join Him, we will also appear in glory! Whatever our past or present, our future will be perfect. Some people await the day when they will walk again; others look forward to hearing or seeing for the first time. Some look forward to thinking with perfect clarity. Others desire healing from depression and anxiety.

🏃 How does your future with Christ encourage you as you think about the change process we outlined last week? Check all that apply.
❑ Someday I'll get it right!
❑ I'm looking forward to _____.
❑ Until then, through the power of the Holy Spirit I will choose to grow day-by-day in my pursuit of Christlikeness.

WHERE SHOULD WE INVEST OUR THOUGHTS?

In the Book of Philippians, Paul described eight types of thoughts that when practiced consistently produce God's peace in our lives. The result for us is anxiety-free living! Read about them in the margin.

Our understanding of each of these eight areas grows over time, as we put them into practice. God knows that mental health depends on keeping our thoughts focused on healthy, positive images. He envisions a process of growth for us through meditating on His Word daily.

1. Things That Are True

Jesus declared that God's Word is true. " 'Sanctify them by the truth; your word is truth' " (John 17:17). People who are truthful in their words and have a sincere character are much more likely to be considered mentally well. Thinking on things that are true will affect how we live. Robert Lewis tells a story about one father who taught his son an important lesson.

> "He tells of an 11-year-old boy eagerly anticipating the opening of bass season. At 10:00 p.m. on the evening before the season opened, the boy practiced casting with his dad from the dock of his family cabin set on a New Hampshire lake. Suddenly, his pole doubled over. He had hooked something … something heavy.
>
> The excitement that followed was absolutely glorious, but nothing compared to the great fish that was lifted from the dark water minutes later. It was the largest bass the boy or his father had ever seen.

"Finally, brothers, whatever is true, whatever is noble, whatever is right, whatever is pure, whatever is lovely, whatever is admirable— if anything is excellent or praiseworthy—think about such things. Whatever you have learned or received or heard from me, or seen in me—put it into practice. And the God of peace will be with you."
—Philippians 4:8-9

The father lit a match and looked at his watch. Then he made this stinging pronouncement: 'You'll have to put it back, son.'

Bass season was two hours away. Just two hours! No one was in sight, so who would know the difference? And yet, the boy's father insisted.

The incident occurred 34 years ago. Never again would the boy catch such a magnificent fish. But what he caught that day was something much better: a lesson in moral character."[1]

In addition to being truthful in your words and actions, being truthful in your thought life means that you do not dwell on untruths. Review the list of unrealistic thinking patterns on page 52.

 On the scale below, evaluate the degree to which you are truthful with yourself in your thoughts.

untruthful   truthful

2. Things That Are Noble

The old word used to describe the act of treating others as if they were royalty is *ennoblement*. To ennoble someone literally means that we raise them to the rank of nobility. Our thoughts should elevate both ourselves and others. The opposite would be thoughts that degrade, lower, or debase ourselves or others.

3. Things That Are Right

A person characterized by understanding finds pleasure in wisdom; it is his or her delight. As a result, wise conduct flows out of a mind that is concentrating its thoughts on what is right in God's eyes. For every positive message we send to those we love, society is sending a contrary message. Our culture is trying to redefine right and wrong as well as the role of the family. William Kilpatrick wrote: "Parents cannot, as they once did, rely on the culture to reinforce home values. In fact, they can expect that many of the cultural forces influencing their children will be actively undermining those values."[2] We must be diligent to pursue righteousness—right living that begins with right thinking.

4. Things That Are Pure

Paul asked us to think about things that are clean, stainless, genuine, and innocent.

 How much of today's entertainment would be excluded if we followed this principle? ❑ none ❑ some ❑ most ❑ all

What thoughts does this principle eliminate?_____

5. Things That Are Lovely

Beauty around us focuses our attention on the mind of our Creator. When it entered into God's mind to create our world, He fashioned it with an abundance of physical beauty. We may not often think in these terms, yet God asks us not only to fulfill tasks, but to perform them in a gracious and lovely manner.[3] God

---

"A fool finds pleasure in
evil conduct,
but a man of understanding
delights in wisdom."
—Proverbs 10:23

INREACH

The next time you are invited to see a movie or video, give yourself the purity test: Will this experience cause my thoughts to dwell on what is clean and innocent?

also wants us to think about things that are truly beautiful. Ugly or displeasing topics do not bring glory to our Creator.

6. Things That Are Admirable

Things that are given a good report are talked about in a positive way. Rather than casting an action or event in a critical light, we are encouraged to focus on the most complimentary description.

Heroes are individuals who put character into action before our eyes. We as Christians ought to admire the heroic. The Bible offers us our best pictures of heroic behavior. We view the actions of David, Esther, Rahab, Gideon, Moses, Joshua, and all the people of faith described in Hebrews 11 in a heroic manner despite their clear human limitations. In fact, only real people with real limitations can be heroes, because true heroes are overcomers.

Week 3 refers to the importance of good books in our quest to be mentally healthy as thinking and growing Christians. A good biography lets us travel through years of a person's life in a few hours. We can know the outcomes of decisions. We can observe integrity rewarded and dishonor brought to ruin. We learn to applaud whatever is admirable.

7. Things That Are Excellent

The idea of heroic character includes the excellent. To excel is to perform at a high level, to attain new heights. Our minds should not just be occupied with what others have achieved but also the excellent or virtuous things that we can do now and into the future.

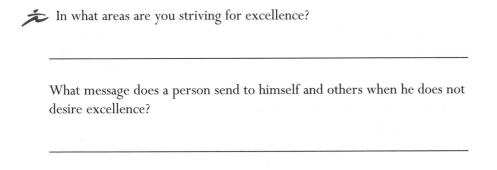 In what areas are you striving for excellence?

_____

What message does a person send to himself and others when he does not desire excellence?

_____

_____

8. Things That Are Praiseworthy

God wants us to learn to praise things that are done well. In other words, when we hear of someone doing a good deed, we ought to think about it and speak well of it. For example: "I heard you brought meals to a new family in your neighborhood when they were involved in a car accident. That was so thoughtful of you!"

 Turn to page 52 and look at the learning exercise you considered in week 6. Which messages did you check? Now, circle those numbers where you are learning to think in a more realistic way.

OUTREACH

Have you praised a family member or coworker today? If not, give someone a blessing by expressing your appreciation for a kind word or deed or a good effort. You will feel blessed in return.

PUT THEM INTO PRACTICE

Paul had a clear strategy for peace in his life. We might call it *a settled mind.* When he was worried and anxious in times of crisis, he would pray about what was troubling him. He encouraged us to do the same. "The peace of God, which transcends all understanding, will guard your hearts and your minds in Christ Jesus" (Phil. 4:7). He assured us that if we allow higher thoughts to govern our actions, the God of peace will be with us (v. 9).

Recall The Stress Model in week 1 (see p. 12). Because we each have the ability to change our thoughts, we can change how we feel. Negative moods, attitudes, and resulting actions can be transformed as we learn to change our thinking.

 For each of the following scenarios, consider the implications of Philippians 4:8-9 as you determine the appropriate mental response and action.

Event	Thoughts	Action
A coworker is telling a dirty joke.		
A fellow Christian is criticizing her pastor.		
You have set an unrealistic goal for yourself.		
Your boss asks you to inflate some statistics.		
You decide to get by without preparing for a Bible study class you attend weekly.		

EXAMINING YOUR MOTIVATION

Many Christians feel defeated in their attempts to control their thought life. They may feel hypocritical: *If people really knew the evil or sinful thoughts I have, they would know how undisciplined I am as a Christian. Sometimes I even question my salvation.*

Our efforts will be more fruitful if we have healthy motivators for mental wellness. Here are two unhealthy motivators that will eventually play out as the basis for transforming the mind.

1. Guilt

Although guilt is often used by others as a weapon to control us, it is a poor motivator. Who wants to please another person out of a sense of guilt? Nowhere in the Bible are we told to serve God out of guilt. Instead, we are told to serve Him out of love and gratitude.

If you feel convicted about the quality of your thought life, the Holy Spirit may be at work in your life seeking to transform your mind. In this case, the proper response is not guilt but repentance. Repentance means to turn around and go in another direction. Repentance is demonstrated by beginning the change process (see week 7).

2. Self-effort

Pulling ourselves up by our boot strings may be the American ideal, but self-effort will take us only so far in transforming our minds. Only through the power of the Holy Spirit can we ever hope to please God with our thought life. Paul reminded us that if righteousness could be attained without Christ's death on the cross, then He died in vain (Gal. 2:21). "There is no one righteous, not even one" (Rom. 3:10).

Many Christians say they believe in salvation by grace alone, yet they live the Christian life as though they will be saved by their works. In a constant attitude of self-introspection, they stack their good deeds beside their bad deeds to determine their status with God at any given time. Christianity is truly unique in its claims that Christ indwells believers in order to empower them to live the Christian life. Other religions encourage adherents to try harder. Aren't we blessed to have Christ's power as our source of strength?

If guilt and self-effort won't sustain us, what will? Here are two healthy motivations that form the basis of transformed minds.

1. Love for God

If you love someone, you want to please him or her. Suddenly it becomes important to know what the person likes or dislikes. You would not willfully offend the object of your affections. In a similar way, our love for God is demonstrated by our desire to please Him. In his study, *Agape Road: Journey to Intimacy with the Father*, Bob Mumford makes a profound statement: "The best and only reliable ally in dealing with temptation is such [love] for the Father that pleasing Him becomes the passion of our lives."[4]

2. Obedience to Him

We want to obey the Father because we are focused on pleasing Him. Obedience grows out of our love relationship. If we have a weak attachment to God, our efforts at obedience will be half-hearted at best. When our passion in life is

UPREACH

Satan wants to keep you in a defeated posture. If you seek victory, you can be assured that he will offer resistance. Recall the importance of putting on God's armor each day (see pages 44-45).

Professor Phitt says:

Our *Fit 4* motto is one wise choice at a time. Don't worry about your obedience tomorrow or the next day. Focus on disciplining your thoughts today. Small successes breed larger successes when we take life one step at time.

intimacy with God, we are no longer driven by worldly desires. We may continue to be drawn to tempting thoughts or sinful deeds, but their hold on us will lessen as we grow our love relationship with God.

In summary, if you are inconsistent or half-hearted in your attempts at thought-control, the secret is not in trying harder or feeling guilty. Success is a byproduct of setting your mind on things above.

Check the ways in which you seek to set your mind on things above.
- ❑ regular personal Bible study
- ❑ regular Bible study with a group
- ❑ Christian books, magazines, tapes
- ❑ worship and praise

- ❑ daily time of prayer
- ❑ Christian music
- ❑ Christian friends
- ❑ service opportunities

❑ other?_____

---

[1] James P. Lenfestey, "Catch of a Lifetime," as told by Robert Lewis in *Raising a Modern-Day Knight* (Wheaton, IL: Tyndale House Publishers, 1997), 64.

[2] William Kilpatrick, *Why Johnny Can't Tell Right from Wrong* (New York: Simon & Schuster, 1992), 252. as quoted by Robert Lewis in *Raising a Modern-Day Knight,* 66.

[3] H.C.G. Moule, *Studies in Philippians* (Grand Rapids, MI: Kregel Publications, 1977), 114.

[4] Bob Mumford, *The Agape Road: Journey to Intimacy with the Father* (Nashville: LifeWay Press, 2000), 113.

Facing High Hurdles

When Judy was diagnosed with clinical depression, her very religious family rejected both her and the diagnosis. They felt a Christian should never be depressed—at least, not for more than a day or two. Their idea of righteousness was in fact a call to cover up or cover over troubling times.

One of the refreshing aspects of the Bible is the blunt descriptions of men and women who loved God and yet were very human in their feelings and actions. Often, we think Paul's life was a spiritual mountaintop from the day in Damascus when he trusted Christ for salvation until his death. Our Verse to Know reflects Paul's confidence in the God of hope. However, in 2 Corinthians Paul offers a frank description of a difficult period in his life.

 Read the margin verses. Underline words that indicate Paul's state of mind. Describe a time when your thoughts were closest to his.

_____

_____

Paul had a deep desire for people to find salvation in Jesus Christ, but even when God had given him an open door to preach the gospel in Troas, he was too restless to stay. He departed from Troas and traveled to Macedonia, which was at least one hundred miles closer to Corinth. He hoped to hear news from his friend Titus concerning the Corinthians, but as he arrived there (2 Cor. 7), he felt even worse: downcast, weary, harassed at every turn, conflicted, and fearful.

We do not know how long this experience lasted for Paul, perhaps days or even weeks, but we do know that God chose to comfort him through a friend and the news that he brought. In a very practical way Paul illustrates how we need to work with others to stay encouraged and to grow. As we seek to increase our understanding of some significant problems that people face, remember that God

VERSE TO KNOW

"May the God of hope fill you with all joy and peace as you trust in him, so that you may overflow with hope by the power of the Holy Spirit."
—Romans 15:13

"When I went to Troas to preach the gospel of Christ and found that the Lord had opened a door for me, I still had no peace of mind, because I did not find my brother Titus there. So I said good-by to them and went on to Macedonia."
—2 Corinthians 2:12-13

"When we came into Macedonia, this body of ours had no rest, but we were harassed at every turn— conflicts on the outside, fears within. But God, who comforts the downcast, comforted us by the coming of Titus."
—2 Corinthians 7:5-6

may want to use you to help someone who faces what I call high hurdles, such as discouragement, depression, anxiety, and distorted thinking.

DO YOU HAVE A HIGH HURDLE TO OVERCOME?

In addition to the fall, temptations, the world, and negative lessons from childhood, we face additional obstacles to loving God with all of our minds. Many people struggle with mental health issues. If you have a difficulty in any of the areas we cover this week, talk with another person about that problem. This person might be a friend, family member, pastor, medical professional, or Christian counselor. Don't let personal pride or embarrassment keep you from available sources of help.

If you have a friend or loved one who struggles with any of these issues, your listening ear can help to lower that hurdle. One of the greatest gifts we can offer others is to seek to hear them and offer a compassionate response.

When people are hindered by mental health problems, they often experience a host of negative emotions: fear, apprehension, embarrassment, confusion, and sadness, to name a few. Often they battle feelings of isolation, shame, or fear because of the self-righteous reactions of well-meaning Christians. These sufferers may feel judged by those who do not battle these high hurdles. We want to step back and look at these problems through the eyes of Jesus. Hopefully, we will grow in love, understanding, and compassion for ourselves and others who face various trials.

 As we begin this study, take a moment to join with me in asking the Father to help us to overcome any apprehensions we might have as we seek help for ourselves or others.

Father, You know the joys and difficulties of everyone You have made. I am humbled by my lack of understanding. Please give me the ability to know myself as You do and to see myself through Your eyes. Increase my compassion and patience for others as well, so I can love You with all of my heart, soul, mind, and strength. Amen.

DEPRESSION

Often, people will say they are depressed when they really mean they are discouraged. Discouragement may last for several days, but most individuals gradually begin to feel more positive about themselves and their circumstances. Clinical depression, on the other hand, is a state of prolonged sadness and despair. Consider the following symptoms of depression.

Symptoms of Depression

To be considered depressed, you would experience five or more symptoms almost every day for two weeks.
1. Depressed mood most of the day, nearly every day for two weeks, person feels sad or empty, cries often.
2. Loss of pleasure in formerly enjoyable activities. In an uncharacteristic manner, the individual becomes bored with work or faces marital difficulty; activities he once enjoyed such as fishing or gardening are now burdensome tasks.

3. Significant changes in weight or appetite. Person has gained 15 pounds, or doesn't feel like eating (a 5 percent change in one month).
4. Can't fall asleep at night, or wakes up repeatedly throughout the night. May sleep too much.
5. Fatigue or loss of energy. Person can't do what they once did; to fix the gate of the fence, or clean the house is overwhelming.
6. Feelings of hopelessness. Person experiences worthlessness, guilt, or withdrawal; pain in being with others with no light at the end of the tunnel.
7. Inability to concentrate or make decisions. Individual may spend an hour on paperwork with no progress. Making simple daily decisions becomes a chore. Sometimes described as *painful thinking.*
8. Recurrent thoughts of death or suicide.[1]

A fairly normal response to discussions on discouragement and depression is for an individual to back away from these topics. Most of us would just as soon focus on brighter days. One reality distinguishes Christianity from all other religions of the world. In other religions a person works to gain something. In Christ a person gains all that is needed for life and lives and works out of love for the Savior. We do not impress God by coming to Him altogether in perfect condition. Instead, He comes to us offering all we need in our state of need.

Life without problems would be ideal—but not realistic. Our intent in this study is to give you some of the tools you will need to discover the hope that God has to offer you. I pray that you will find Him to be "the God of hope" (Rom. 15:13).

The biblical answer for the person who feels discouraged or depressed is hope. Paul is mindful of this when he prayed for the Roman believers in this week's Verse to Know. Read it again on page 69.

Professor Phitt says:
The *Fit 4* plan focuses on fitness and nutrition, two important ingredients in overcoming depression. Depression can work to take a person off of their fitness and nutrition programs. This is why it is helpful to work in a group with others for mutual support and encouragement.

What is the source of our hope? _____

By whose power do we overflow with this hope?_____

What is the key to being filled with joy and peace? _____

For more information on this subject, study the book I coauthored with Paul Carlisle, *Strength for the Journey: A Biblical Perspective on Discouragement and Depression.*"[2] In the book, we point out that hope is the emotional component of faith. Hope is faith directed toward the future. Discovering hope involves (1) listening to the encouraging words found in the Bible; and (2) persevering in your daily walk with God. That means hanging in there!

Hope is faith directed toward the future.

If you found yourself identifying with one or more of the symptoms of depression, take the self-test on the following page. You can use it to evaluate either yourself or someone close to you.

SELF-TEST: Symptoms of Depression

On the following continuums circle the number that reflects your present experience with each symptom.

1. Loss of pleasure in formerly enjoyable activities.

1   2   3   4   5
infrequent   frequent

2. Changes in weight or appetite.

1   2   3   4   5
none   much

3. Changes in sleep patterns.

1   2   3   4   5
none   much

4. Fatigue or loss of energy.

1   2   3   4   5
none   much

5. Feelings of hopelessness, worthlessness, or guilt.

1   2   3   4   5
infrequent   frequent

6. Inability to concentrate.

1   2   3   4   5
infrequent   frequent

7. Recurrent thoughts of death or suicide.

1   2   3   4   5
infrequent   frequent

If you circled numbers 3, 4, or 5 on five or more of these symptoms, it may indicate that your depression is serious enough for you to seek professional help. This is especially true if the symptoms have persisted daily for two weeks. You would be wise to see a doctor for a health checkup, since medical science continues to make progress in treating mental health issues that have a physical root or component. Often, depressed thoughts that are not associated with clinical depression arise from a pattern of distorted thinking, which you may have learned from significant others and have continued into adulthood. See pages 74-76 for help in changing distorted thinking patterns into thoughts that glorify God.

ANXIETY

🏃 Place an X on the line which suggests the degree of anxiety that you experience on a regular basis.

I am not a worrier.   I worry too much.   I am frequently overcome by extreme panic.

Anxiety is another obstacle to loving God with all of our minds. However, God is not the enemy of the anxious person but a loving ally. It is in this spirit of loving support and encouragement that Paul said, "Do not be anxious about anything, but in everything, by prayer and petition, with thanksgiving, present your requests to God. And the peace of God, which transcends all understanding, will guard your hearts and your minds in Christ Jesus" (Phil. 4:6). Several key points in this passage can be of great benefit to the person hindered by anxiety and worry.

1. **God wants to hear about your problem.** When we are anxious about something, God invites us to talk with Him about that person or thing. In other words, Paul is not offering a rebuke by saying, *Anxiety is a sin, so cut it out!* It is more along the lines of, *Don't keep your anxious worries to yourself; open your heart to God and let Him know all that is troubling you.*
2. **God promises peace.** We do not arrive at the peace of God by our own efforts; He must give it to us. Our part is to pray for peace.
3. **God protects our minds.** God guards our hearts and minds in Christ Jesus when we talk to God about our problems. He takes our troubled thoughts and replaces them with His peace.

Symptoms of Anxiety

The following symptoms are common for someone who is overly anxious. If these symptoms persist for you, consult your medical doctor in case your anxiety is related to some other medical condition.

1. **Tension:** shakiness, jitteriness, trembling, inability to relax, restlessness, and muscle aches
2. **Heart pounding or racing:** Sweating, hyperactivity, cold or clammy hands, dry mouth, dizziness, upset stomach, frequent urination, diarrhea, lump in the throat, tingling in hands, light-headedness
3. **Worry:** fear, recurrent thoughts, anticipation of misfortune to self or others
4. **Irritability:** Difficulty concentrating, distraction, insomnia, impatience

If your anxiety is not medically based, it may be related to a situation you are facing. Certainly, taking finals in a college course may cause anxiety, as does waiting outside the intensive care ward for news about a loved one, or concerns about a

UPREACH
Have you begun or continued the discipline of daily prayer and Bible study? These actions of meditation have been shown to lower blood pressure and elevate one's mood.

lay-off in your industry. However, anxiety that is not related to a specific cause may require professional assistance. Many appropriate therapies are available to treat panic attacks or persistent worrisome thoughts.

DISTORTED THINKING

I mentioned earlier that distorted thinking may play a role in depression. It can also impact anxiety levels. The way we think has dramatic influence on the way we feel and act. We can predict the course of distorted thinking and its consequences. We can also change distorted thinking to glorify God. The following description, adapted from A. T. Beck's *Cognitive Therapy of Depression,*[3] illustrates how distorted thinking can be interrupted and changed to a positive and healthy thought process.

1. What happened? What event led to the distorted thinking?
    Someone criticized my presentation at work.
2. What was my reaction? What emotions did I feel?
    I was ashamed of myself. I felt I had performed badly.
3. What thought preceded my emotions?
    I'll never amount to anything. I'm no good at what I do.
4. Was that thought rational or realistic?
    I have consistently received positive performance evaluations and accompanying raises based on achieving my objectives. Perhaps my presentation was flawed or perhaps the critical person gave a faulty evaluation. I must ask more questions and get additional feedback.
5. Based on changing my thoughts, did my emotions change?
    I feel more hopeful about how I performed and more motivated to improve.
6. Based on changing my thoughts, did my actions change?
    Since I wasn't upset, I didn't eat a second bowl of ice cream.

Try this exercise based on a recent experience, or complete it when you encounter your next stressful event:

1. What happened?_____

2. What emotions did I feel?_____

3. What thought preceded my emotions?_____

4. Was that thought rational or realistic? (circle)   yes   no

5. Based on changing my thoughts, how did my emotions change?

    _____

6. Based on changing my thoughts, how did my actions change?

    _____

INREACH

One of the best motivators for changing distorted thinking is to remind ourselves of God's truth. Satan comes to us to steal, kill, and destroy, but Christ gives abundant life (John 10:10). Satan wants your mind. Will you give it to Christ instead?

We can change the angry, fearful, hopeless, or sinful thoughts in our minds. We are not victims of the thoughts that come into our heads, but rather we take those thoughts captive for Christ. Each thought presents us with a new opportunity to choose mental wellness. We can exchange negative thinking patterns for ones that dwell on healthy, positive images: love for anger, peace for fear, hope for hopelessness, trust for worry, gratitude for envy.

The key word is *choice*. God gives us freedom to choose. We can choose His way to transformed minds or we can choose to remain locked in distorted thinking that produces inner and outer conflict. Each of us must deal with our resistance to change. Even negative thinking patterns are comfort zones if we have lived with them for years. We may have to confront the value we have placed on holding onto grievances, blaming others, or condemning ourselves.

Have you found yourself unwilling to let go of certain thought patterns? (circle)   yes   no

If so, identify them._____

_____

What benefits do you feel you get from these patterns?

_____

_____

What would you gain if you changed these patterns?

_____

_____

What keeps us in bondage is our attachment to these patterns. We believe we gain some benefit from these negative thoughts. Yearning to be free will not make the critical difference. We must exchange the lie for the truth: These patterns are not our friends but the enemies of a healthy thought life.

Recall that Satan wants control of your mind. You must wear the armor of God to resist his efforts to neutralize your witness for Christ (Eph. 6:10-18). You must repent of thoughts that do not honor God. Repentance is the process of turning around and going in a different direction.

Take responsibility for your own thoughts rather than blaming others for what has happened in the past or is presently occurring. Acknowledge that it is not other people or events that need to change in order for you to be happy. Rather, you can choose what you put into your mind, how you interpret the world (your

> Each thought presents us with a new opportunity to choose mental wellness.

worldview), and how you respond to it. You can choose to limit the influence of the world and negative people by focusing on God and maintaining healthy Christian friendships.

These realizations can literally affect every aspect of our lives. As we heal distorted thoughts and seek the "mind of Christ" (1 Cor. 2:16), we can then genuinely affirm that we are seeking to love God with all our minds.

 Do you need to repent of a recurring thought pattern? If so, ask God for His forgiveness. Choose to honor Him with your thoughts. Ask Him for His power to bring about this renewing of your mind.

ADDITIONAL HIGH HURDLES

A number of mental health issues can limit loving God with all our minds: schizophrenia, paranoia, bipolar (manic-depressive), and neuroses such as perfectionism or obsessive-compulsive disorder.

Persons facing these high hurdles need our compassion, patience, and loving care. Treatment usually requires medical and psychological/psychiatric intervention. If you are in a position to befriend such a person, encourage him or her to continue with prescribed medication and/or the recommended treatment plan. Because of impaired thinking, these individuals may lack judgment regarding their care; some may require temporary or extended institutional care.

Other people struggle with problems related to brain injury/trauma.

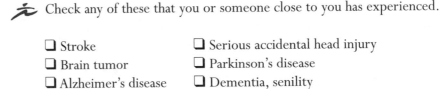 Check any of these that you or someone close to you has experienced.

❏ Stroke   ❏ Serious accidental head injury
❏ Brain tumor   ❏ Parkinson's disease
❏ Alzheimer's disease   ❏ Dementia, senility
❏ Other?_____

Trauma to the brain may impair walking, speech, and other physical movements. Often extensive physical and occupational therapy may be required. Some individuals may regain full use of their faculties while others may remain limited for the rest of their lives.

Some Christians are more tolerant of persons with physical impairments than those with mental impairments. In fact, mental health issues are often the subjects of ridicule, humor, or judgmentalism. Families who have a loved one with a mental disorder have been known to hide that information or talk about it only in private conversation.

 Why do you think these families feel shame?

_____

OUTREACH

Think of a person who encouraged you at a low point in your life. Write a note, email, or phone this person and express your thanks.

What can we do as a Christian community to minister to individuals and families facing these high hurdles?

SPIRITUAL MISCONCEPTIONS

Let's deal with two common misconceptions about mental health sufferers.

1. Are people with mental health problems greater sinners?

Most of us would quickly answer this question, *No, of course not!* However, many believers who face long-term mental health problems confront this question. In the Book of Job, Job faced the judgment of others when he began to face difficulties. Although Job faced various trials, health problems were Job's greatest test of faith. His entire body was covered with sore boils to such an extent that his friends could barely recognize him. Just the sight of him brought them to tears (2:7-13).

At the beginning of the Book of Job, he is described as a man of high integrity and character. If the price of sin were ill-health, we would expect Job to be in perfect health! His friends attempted to blame Job's struggles on his own sin. In the end God rebuked these sorry comforters who didn't understand His work in Job's life.

If you struggle with physical or mental health issues or can reflect back on a time when you did, you probably wondered if your personal failings had brought on the condition. In fact, when people are struggling and need God the most, their affliction will often leave them feeling distant from Him.

Because Job felt distanced from God, he needed comfort from his friends rather than rebuke. When God places us in the lives of people who are suffering ill-health, we need to be quick to offer support and encouragement. While it is true that an undisciplined lifestyle can result in health problems, people suffer many difficulties they had absolutely no control over.

2. Do mental health problems indicate a lack of faith?

All sickness can ultimately be traced to the fall. When Adam sinned in the garden, the punishment was death. Bodies became susceptible to many different kinds of sickness and disease. Human error led to accidents and mishaps. Although God expects us to display faith—"Without faith it is impossible to please God" (Heb. 11:6)—no clear pattern in the Bible associates healing exclusively with the faith of the one being healed. Jesus, the disciples, and Paul the apostle performed miracles where the faith of the one receiving healing was not a factor (see Luke 7:11-15, Acts 3:1-8, Acts 16:16-18). The truth from Scripture is that God did not always heal; even when He did heal, the individual still died at some point in time; and death itself is a form of healing (Rev. 21:4).

> "In the land of Uz there lived a man whose name was Job. This man was blameless and upright; he feared God and shunned evil."
> —Job 1:1

"Praise be to the God and Father of our Lord Jesus Christ, the Father of compassion and the God of all comfort, who comforts us in all our troubles, so that we can comfort those in any trouble with the comfort we ourselves have received from God."
—2 Corinthians 1:3-4

God responds to suffering with compassion. Paul writes about God's compassion toward those who are afflicted in 2 Corinthians 1:3-4. Read this passage in the margin, paying special attention to the word comfort.

Three important lessons on God's comfort are found in this passage:
1. He is the God of all comfort.
2. He comforts us in all our troubles.
3. He has prepared us to be ministers of His comfort.

Note that we are called to minister God's comfort to those who are facing trouble. Even if we have not faced the same trouble that a friend is going through, we can still support, encourage, and comfort him or her.

 Thank the Lord that He looks on your troubles with compassion. Write the names of two people you know who are facing mental health issues. Then write one way you can offer comfort.

Name	Way to Offer Comfort
1.	
2.	

[1]Adapted from the American Psychiatric Association (1994). *Diagnostic and Statistical Manual of Mental Disorders* (DSM-IV).

[2]Dr. James P. Porowski and Dr. Paul B. Carlisle, *Strength For The Journey* (Nashville: LifeWay, 1999) 150-152.

[3]Aaron T. Beck, *Cognitive Therapy of Depression* (New York: Guilford Press, 1979) 403.

Loving God with All Your Mind

In week 1 we learned that our thoughts cannot be separated from our hearts (emotions), souls (spiritual selves), or bodies. When we direct every aspect of our lives to God—heart, soul, mind, and strength—He is the one who holds the different components in balance.

The mind influences the whole person. How you and I think will move our hearts, persuade our spirits, and effect our bodies in significant ways. Isaiah linked the idea of personal peace with a steadfast mind. Perhaps the words from Isaiah 26:3-4 were on Paul's mind when he encouraged us to enjoy God's peace by praying during anxious times and maintaining an upward focus during the daily traffic of life (Phil. 4:6-9). Ultimately, peace is a by-product of trust in God.

In this study I chose to use Paul's writings to provide focus and continuity. Paul was uniquely selected by God to bridge the gap between Jewish and Gentile thinking as a teacher of three worlds: Jewish, Greek, and Roman. I hope that through this study, Paul's thinking has entered your world and been your teacher.

Recall that when Paul made his defense before the governor, Festus, and King Agrippa, Festus declared with astonishment, "You are out of your mind, Paul! … Your great learning is driving you insane." To this Paul quickly responded and set the matter straight, "I am not insane, most excellent Festus," (Acts 26:24-25). I hope that you can say the same for yourself after this study! Our goal has been to grasp the key role that our minds and thought processes play in living out our commitment to Christ. When our thought patterns do not enhance our relationship with Him or others, they must be transformed into wholesome and productive thoughts (Phil. 4:8).

HOW THE MIND WORKS

In week 2 we explored how the mind works. Our discussion was centered on the physiology of the brain and the idea of personality. While our understanding of the human brain has grown considerably since Paul's time, it is founded on what he already knew: God made us, and our discoveries point to His incredible work.

"God has arranged the parts in the body, every one of them, just as he wanted them to be. If they were all one part, where would the body be? As it is, there are many parts, but one body."
—1 Corinthians 12:18-20

Billions of cells work together in our brains to produce thoughts. Thoughts are physical in nature and control the body, while the body in turn sends messages to the mind (see pgs. 16-17). But we are more than machines. God created us with a spirit, and to those who have been born anew in Christ, He also gave His Holy Spirit to live in them. This combination makes us mental, physical, and spiritual beings.

Recall from pages 19-23 how each of these shapes our personalities:

traits/temperament _____

_____

how a person is reared _____

_____

God created us to think and learn. But we are not like stalks of corn in a field, with each plant looking pretty much like the next one. Each of us has our own personality. Paul applied this concept to the church. The church is a body, and our individual gifts and differences actually make the body work as a whole.

MENTAL FITNESS

In weeks 3 and 4 we described characteristics of those who love God with all their minds. I called this *mental fitness*. Paul told us that we have the mind of Christ (1 Cor. 2:16). God has enabled us through His Spirit to relate to Him and others in a new and productive way.

1. **God has motivated us to seek after godly wisdom** and promises that the one who passionately looks for wisdom will be happily rewarded (Prov. 2:1-6).

2. **God has called us to process life through a biblical worldview.** Christians should not be afraid to explore the world. We can have confidence that learning and discovering will work for God's glory, as His greatness and glory are demonstrated to us. God wants us to explore, uncover, and think about His creation from the vantage point of our fallenness and redemption in Christ.

3. **God has called us to continue on a steady course of learning and growing.** While God's greatness is revealed in what He has hidden, our greatness is revealed in what we discover (Prov. 25:2). We have a need to think and learn because this is how God made us.

4. **God wants us to have a healthy view of ourselves** by keeping in mind three important principles. **First,** God wants us to grow in the understanding of how much Jesus loves us. **Second,** God wants us to live our lives in a balanced manner. As we walk by faith in the light of His Word, we establish priorities and stick with them! **Third,** the Lord wants us to enjoy relationships with others. Maintaining supportive ties with healthy people helps to ensure healthy

self-perceptions. With good Christian friends. we are more likely to have a realistic outlook on life.

5. **God wants us to love others as we love ourselves.** *Fit 4* seeks to balance INREACH and OUTREACH as we continue our UPREACH to God. Our goal is to be other-centered rather than self-centered. Living in a humble and unassuming manner is characterized by considering the major needs and concerns of others.

6. **God wants us to maintain healthy boundaries with others.** Even humility and others-centeredness must be kept in balance! Boundaries are limits that we set on ourselves so that our energies are not exhausted. If we are constantly running on empty, eventually we will be sidelined in serving God and others. Boundaries indicate that we love *ourselves* as well as others.

 On page 14 you were asked to evaluate yourself in the following areas of mental wellness. Compare your responses now with your responses at the end of week 1. Place an X at the appropriate spot.

A growing relationship with God

Weakness   Strength

A healthy view of myself

Weakness   Strength

A genuine love and concern for others

Weakness   Strength

OBSTACLES TO LOVING GOD WITH OUR MINDS

In weeks 5 and 6 we centered our attention on the obstacles we face in seeking to love God with all our minds. Remember that Paul encouraged us no longer to live in the futility of our thinking, as non-believers live (Eph. 4:17). As Christians, we can choose to think productively and effectively. To overcome the obstacles we face, we must have a good understanding of these hindrances.

1. **We must understand that we are fallen.** The second characteristic of a Christian worldview answers the question, "what has gone wrong with the world?" by stating, "humanity has fallen" (see p. 29). Each one of us has a fallen nature. When we turn to Christ for salvation, we have the capacity to follow Him in obedience, but the old nature remains with its tendency to sin.

2. **We must understand that we face temptations.** Daily we risk being deceived in our thinking, but we resist temptation by renewing our minds and setting our minds on God. God will not allow us to be tempted beyond our capacity to endure and will provide us with a way out (1 Cor. 10:13).

INREACH

Put a check by the obstacle you struggle with the most. Consider reading again the pages of this workbook that apply to that obstacle.

3. **We must understand that we are influenced by the world.** We are besieged each day by images from the media of false standards of beauty, worth, and success. If we have not replaced the world's thinking with God's truth, our ideas concerning morality and life's priorities will be influenced negatively.

4. **We must examine distortions of reality we learned growing up.** When children are reared with unrealistic standards and distorted thinking, they may form false images of themselves and others. Paul warned fathers against embittering and discouraging children (Eph. 6:4; Col. 3:21). Our families have a great need for careful, Christ-centered parenting. As children are reared in the "training and instruction of the Lord" (Eph. 6:4), discipline benefits the child when it is administered in love.

 Record what you can do to overcome these obstacles by listing one or more Action P's (Promise to claim, Prayer to make, Person to encourage/ be encouraged by).

Obstacles	Action P's
I have a sin nature	
I face temptations.	
I am influenced by the world.	
I am affected by past experiences.	

A PROCESS FOR CHANGE

In weeks 7 and 8 we learned that change involves daily choices and a healthy upward focus on Christ. Negative moods and attitudes can be transformed as we learn to change our thinking.

1. **We conform ourselves to God's thinking.** In Romans 12:1-2, we looked at three points emphasized by Paul in transforming a depraved mind into one that is controlled by God's Spirit. **First,** change begins as we offer our bodies as living sacrifices to God. **Second,** we are transformed by the renewing of our minds. We can either turn our minds to the world, ruled by darkness, or to

"I urge you, brothers, in view of God's mercy, to offer your bodies as living sacrifices, holy and pleasing to God—which is your spiritual worship. Do not conform any longer to the pattern of this world, but be transformed by the renewing of your mind. Then you will be able to test and approve what God's will is—his good, pleasing and perfect will."
—Romans 12:1-2

Christ and the control of His Spirit. **Third,** we experience the joy of living out God's will. When you and I choose to yield our minds to God's control, we discover His goodness and love.

2. **We use the model for change in view of Romans 12:2.** The model for change has four stages: Develop awareness, Grow in knowledge and understanding, take action, and experience change.

3. **We set our minds on things above.** When we focus our attention upward, we see our past, present, and future centered in Christ (Col. 3:1-4). Paul described what our hearts recognize as we look at Jesus seated at the right hand of God. In the **past** we died (v. 3). People with an upward focus are aware that their past is behind them. **Today** our life is hidden with Christ in God, safe and secure. In the **future** Christ will appear in glory; we will also appear in glory with Him.

4. **We determine to keep our thoughts focused in the right places.** Because God asks us to meditate on His Word daily, we can assume that He envisions a process of daily growth for us. Paul made sure that his mind was set on things that were true, noble, right, pure, lovely, admirable, excellent, and praiseworthy (Phil. 4:8-9). He assured us that if we do the same, focusing our thoughts in the right places and allowing them to govern our actions, the God of peace will be with us.

Professor Phitt says:
Presenting ourselves as a "living sacrifice" (Rom. 12:1) represents our commitment to being good stewards of our bodies. Continue to practice healthy eating choices and regular exercise when this study concludes. Use your *Accountability Journal* to chart your progress.

Consider again some important points in the process for change. Identify the extent to which these change processes are a part of your life. Place a check in the appropriate box.

I offer myself to God as a living sacrifice, holy and pleasing to God.

❑ Not at all ❑ Sometimes ❑ Most of the time

I conform my thoughts to God's will.

❑ Not at all ❑ Sometimes ❑ Most of the time

I identify areas of needed change and work through the change process.

❑ Not at all ❑ Sometimes ❑ Most of the time

I set my mind on things above, where Christ sits at God's right hand.

❑ Not at all ❑ Sometimes ❑ Most of the time

I keep my thoughts focused in the right places.

❑ Not at all ❑ Sometimes ❑ Most of the time

FACING HIGH HURDLES

In week 9 we learned that Paul's life and ministry did not consist of continuous spiritual mountaintop experiences. In 2 Corinthians 2:12-13 he described a period in which he had no peace of mind. God may want us to encourage someone who faces what I call high hurdles, such as discouragement, depression, and anxiety.

Someone close to you may even struggle with problems related to brain injury or trauma, or disorders that require medical intervention. Remember that people with health problems are not greater sinners, and the existence of health-related problems does not indicate a lack of faith.

When depressive or negative thinking patterns result from distorted thinking, we can learn to change the way we think by employing the concepts listed on pages 74-76. Identifying irrational or distorted thinking, rejecting those thoughts as Satan's lies, and replacing them with God's truth enables us to experience positive thoughts and emotions that glorify God.

 Review the learning activity on page 74. Have you used this process to identify and change a distorted thought since you completed week 9? (circle)   yes   no

If so, tell about your experience.

_____

_____

Have you practiced exchanging a negative thinking pattern such as worry or fear for a positive one? (circle)   yes   no

If so, what benefits do you feel you have received?

_____

_____

UPREACH
Explain how loving God puts all of life—including our thought life—into perspective.

Instead of being victims of the thoughts that come into our heads, we can take those thoughts captive for Christ. Each thought represents a new opportunity to choose mental wellness. We can exchange negative thinking patterns for patterns that glorify God.

If we can choose positive thinking patterns, do you recall why many of us choose to remain locked in distorted thinking that produces inner and outer conflict? We are resistant to change, even when the change would benefit us greatly. Negative thinking patterns become comfort zones that we must confront in order to break free. Repentance is agreeing with God's opinion about our thoughts. Then, in genuine remorse, we begin the daily process of renewing our minds.

HAVING A TRANSFORMED MIND

God created us with the capacity for giving and receiving love. One of the greatest thoughts that our minds can entertain is loving and being loved by someone else. God wants us to love Him above anyone or anything else because loving Him puts everything else in life in perspective. In Him, we find the hope, peace, and joy that is only possible through a personal relationship with God. Through His presence in our lives, we can truly love others, because God is love. Love comes from God (1 John 4:7-8).

If you have not yet made the decision to receive God's love gift to you by accepting Jesus Christ as your Lord and Savior, turn to page 87 and read How to Become a Christian. I pray that today will be the day you begin to renew your mind.

Once you have made this commitment, daily focus on growing in your relationship with God through Bible study, prayer, and discipleship studies such as the one you have just completed.

For those of you who have been Christians for weeks, months, or years, your progress in Christlikeness may seem painfully slow at times. There is no magic bullet to spur your growth because it is based on relationship with God. If your relationship bonds are weak and your prayer life sporadic, your growth will be small. However, if you continue your UPREACH, INREACH, and OUTREACH in the spirit of Mark 12:30-31, growth will continue at a steady pace.

OUTREACH
What effect will changing distorted thinking have on your relationships with

Family? _____

_____

Coworkers? _____

_____

Fellow believers? _____

_____

 The concepts presented in this book have been based on the premises listed below. Match each premise with the Scripture that supports it. (Answers are found at the bottom of this page.)

____ 1. We have the mind of Christ.

    a. 2 Corinthians 10:5

____ 2. We choose the thoughts that we dwell on.

    b. Philippians 4:8;
       Ephesians 4:22-24

____ 3. We can take those thoughts captive for Christ.

    c. 1 Corinthians 2:16

____ 4. This process involves a daily commitment to Christ's rule in our lives.

    d. Colossians 2:6

A renewed mind really is a matter of the will. As a result of this study, you have the knowledge of how the change process works. Now you must *will* to work the process. Rather than concentrating on the goal—a renewed mind—concentrate on taking each thought captive.

(Answers to activity: 1. c; 2. b; 3. a; 4. d)

"Therefore, if anyone is
in Christ, he is a new
creation; the old has gone,
the new has come!"
—2 Corinthians 5:17

ONE WISE THOUGHT AT A TIME

I hope that you can say this study has helped you to grow as a thinking Christian. I hope that you find yourself further along in your quest to follow Christ in His great commandment: " 'Love the Lord your God with all your heart and with all your soul and with all your mind and with all your strength.' The second is this: 'Love your neighbor as yourself' " (Mark 12:30-31).

Our *Fit 4* motto is one wise choice at a time. In mental fitness, perhaps we could rephrase the motto: one wise thought at a time. The battle for the mind is won one thought at a time. Try to focus your mental energies on today, rather than worrying about your success tomorrow or failures of yesterday. You are on a wellness journey. Arriving is not as important as the process by which you get there. May I close this study by praying for all of us.

> *Father, I pray that we would claim Your power to renew our minds. As new creations, help us to honor You with our thoughts. Strengthen us daily in our journey toward loving You with all our minds. Amen.*

How to Become a Christian

One of our greatest satisfactions on earth is knowing and living God's truth. When we believe and practice distorted thinking—based on past experiences, our personal choices, or our sin nature—life simply does not work the way God intended. We were created as spiritual beings with a capacity to know and love God. Because we were made to be like God, we have an empty spot in our lives until we find fulfillment in Him. In Jesus Christ, we find the hope, peace, and joy that is only possible through a personal relationship with God.

John 3:16 says, "'God so loved the world that he gave his one and only Son, that whoever believes in him shall not perish but have eternal life.'" In order to live our earthly lives "to the full" (see John 10:10), we must accept God's gift of love.

A relationship with God begins by admitting that we are not perfect and continue to fall short of God's standards. Romans 3:23 says, "All have sinned and fall short of the glory of God." The price for these wrongdoings is separation from God. We deserve to pay the price for our sin. "The wages (or price) of sin is death, but the gift of God is eternal life in Christ Jesus our Lord" (Rom. 6:23).

God's love comes to us right in the middle of our sin. "God demonstrates his own love for us in this: While we were still sinners, Christ died for us" (Rom. 5:8). He doesn't ask us to clean up our lives first—in fact, without His help, we are incapable of living by His standards. He wants us to come to Him as we are.

Forgiveness begins when we admit our sin to God. When we do, He is faithful to forgive and restore our relationship with Him. "If we confess our sins, he is faithful and just and will forgive us our sins and purify us from all unrighteousness" (1 John 1:9).

Scripture confirms that this love gift and relationship with God is not just for a special few, but for everyone. "Everyone who calls on the name of the Lord will be saved" (Romans 10:13).

If you would like to receive God's gift of salvation, pray this prayer:

> *Dear God, I know that I am imperfect and separated from You. Please forgive me of my sin and adopt me as Your child. Thank You for this gift of life through the sacrifice of Your Son. I will live my life for You. Amen.*

If you prayed this prayer for the first time, you are now a child of God. In your Bible, read 1 John 5:11-12. This verse assures you that if you have accepted God's Son, Jesus Christ, as your Savior and Lord, you have this eternal life.

Share your experience with your *Fit 4* facilitator, someone in your group, your pastor, or a trusted Christian friend. Welcome to God's family!

Leader Guide

With All My Mind: God's Design for Mental Wellness is a continuing study in *Fit 4: A LifeWay Christian Wellness Plan.* This study is open to anyone who chooses to participate, whether or not the person has taken another *Fit 4* course or continuing study. Treat it as you would any one-hour group discipleship course.

Relationship to *Fit 4*

Review pages 4 and 5 to understand how this study incorporates the basic principles of *Fit 4.*

Because this study emphasizes only one of four essential components of wellness, encourage participants to use the *Accountability Journal* provided with each member book to record daily food and exercise choices. Some participants may not have committed to the *Fit 4* Guidelines for Healthy Eating (see *Journal,* p. 20) or the *Fit 4* F.I.T.T. exercise model for developing a personalized exercise plan (see *Journal,* p. 14). Promote the concept of whole-person health by encouraging nutritional and fitness goals as an integral part of total wellness. The Professor Phitt suggestions each week offer practical application activities.

Introductory Session

Because of the *Fit 4* terminology used, as well as references to Professor Phitt and other *Fit 4* resources, we recommend that participants view the 15-minute *Fit 4* Introductory Session video found at the beginning of both the *Fitness* and *Nutrition* group session videos in the *Fit 4 Plan Kit* (ISBN 0-6330-0580-0). Preview the video and have it cued at the beginning of the tape. Arrange for a TV/VCR for the introductory session only. A lesson plan for the introductory session is found on page 89.

Sessions 1-10

Each week's reading assignment can be read in one sitting or spaced throughout the week. Encourage participants to memorize the Verse(s) to Know and say the Scripture together at the beginning of each session. Session plans for the 10 weeks are found on pages 89-94. They are guides to help you lead discussion.

Encourage participants to ask questions and make comments from their reading. The benefit to each participant will increase as he or she completes each lesson's margin

Lifestyle Discipline activities as well as the learning activities highlighted by the *Fit 4* logo. Calling attention to these elements of the lesson will promote their use. Otherwise, members may assume they are unimportant.

Leading the Wrap-Up Session

Session 11 (week 12 of the study) is the final session of each *Fit 4* continuing course. In this session, lead a time of sharing, reflection, planning for the future, and praying. Several ideas for informal closure activities are suggested on page 94. Review these a few weeks before session 11 so you can plan ahead. Include the class in the planning.

Your Role as Facilitator

Like other members of your group, you are on your own wellness journey. No one is looking to you as an expert on mental wellness. Your role is to guide the group experience using the session plans provided.

Before each session, arrive early. Place chairs in a circle and sit with other members. Provide a sign-up sheet at the door and name tags, if needed. Have on hand extra Bibles, pens or pencils, and member books for the first two sessions. Pray for each member, the group process, and yourself on a regular basis. Use the attendance sheet to note absentees; then contact them during the week.

Begin and end each session on time. Open and close the sessions with prayer. Encourage member discussion of the week's material. Avoid doing too much talking. Keep the discussion positive, in keeping with the emphasis on mental wellness. Avoid letting members get too personal or graphic in sharing.

Be aware of special needs in the class. If a class member is unsaved, be prepared to follow the leadership of the Holy Spirit to know the right time to talk to that person privately to lead them to Christ (see How to Become a Christian, p. 87). If other problems surface, be prepared to refer members to Christian counselors in the area.

After the session, complete your weekly reading assignment and your *Accountability Journal.* Learn each week's Verse(s) to Know. Follow the instructions in this Guide for planning for the next session.

INTRODUCTORY SESSION

Session Goals

To introduce participants to the concept of whole-person health based on Mark 12:30-31 and to enlist participation in this study.

Before the Session

- Set up the TV/VCR and cue the tape to the Introductory Session video.
- Arrange chairs so everyone can see the TV screen and each other.
- Supply name tags for each person.
- Provide an attendance sheet and pen.
- Have on hand one copy of the member book and *Accountability Journal* for every person expected.
- Before members arrive, pray for God's guidance.

During the Session

Greet members as they arrive. Have them sign the attendance sheet and give a phone number or email address. Instruct them to complete and wear the provided name tag. Open with prayer.

Introduce yourself and ask participants to share their names and one interesting fact about themselves. Distribute copies of *With All My Mind: God's Design for Mental Wellness* and the *Accountability Journal*.

Explain that although this study is open to anyone, it is a continuing study in *Fit 4: A LifeWay Christian Wellness Plan*. Say: *During this session we will watch the Fit 4 Introductory Session video to acquaint you with the concept of whole-person health and to introduce you to terms that will be used throughout the study.* Ask members to turn to page 6 in their Member Books and write responses on the Viewer Guide as you play the Introductory Session video.

Ask volunteers to share responses to the Viewer Guide. Review pages 4 and 5 of the Member Book. Instruct participants to put their *Accountability Journals* in a three-ring binder. Highlight the information on pages 4-25. Explain that the *Accountability Journal* is a voluntary tool to encourage a wellness lifestyle. No one will evaluate their entries. Ask them to turn to page 26, circle tomorrow's day, and write the date. Encourage the group to begin tomorrow recording their food and exercise choices.

Overview week 1 having participants turn through the pages as you talk about various sections. Explain the purpose of the Verses to Know and the margin activities. Point out that the material can be read in one sitting or by sections throughout the week. Call attention to page 95, which lists other *Fit 4* resources, such as the fit4.com Web site and the *Christian Health* magazine.

Allow time for participants to ask questions. Collect payment for materials, if needed. Close the session with a word of encouragement and prayer.

SESSION I

Session Goals

To understand how the mind influences the whole person: body, emotions, and spirit. To appreciate the importance of mental wellness in whole-person health.

During the Session

As members arrive, ask them to sign the attendance sheet and wear a name tag (optional). Allow 2-3 minutes for prayer requests and enlist a volunteer to pray.

Say or read together the Verses to Know (p.7). Ask someone to recall why the apostle Paul was uniquely selected by God to teach new believers in Christ.

Review key points from each of the major headings by asking questions such as: How does the mind influence the whole person? Emphasize specific statements you may have underlined as you read.

Ask members to turn to the learning exercise on page 13. Ask volunteers to share what they wrote. Then ask, *How might different thoughts change those emotions?*

Enlist volunteers to share their responses to **UPREACH, OUTREACH,** and **INREACH** activities in the margin. Ask if anyone followed Professor Phitt's advice to set nutrition or fitness goals for the next 10 weeks. Review the three areas of mental wellness on page 13, relating them to the Verses to Know on page 7.

Overview session 2, creating interest in the topic and assigning it to be read for session 2. Close with prayer.

SESSION 2

Session Goals

To affirm that God is the creator of our minds. To understand two characteristics of the mind: the physiology of the brain and the idea of personality.

During the Session

Greet members and have them sign the attendance sheet. Call for prayer requests and enlist a volunteer to pray. Say or read together the Verse to Know (p. 15).

Ask, Why have secular philosophers compared people to machines? In what ways are we like machines? How can we be compared to a computer? What makes us different from machines?

Invite reactions to this statement on page 17: "The Holy Spirit enables our minds to understand God's will and to communicate with Him. God has given us the ability to love Him with all our minds." Ask members to list ways God helps us to fulfill Mark 12:30-31.

Encourage volunteers to share answers to the learning exercise on page 18. Ask them to explain how unhealthy data can be replaced by healthy data.

Ask, *Which do you think is most important in shaping a person's personality, God-given traits/temperament or how a person is reared?* Allow for differences of opinion.

Ask members to share which personality characteristics listed on page 20 best describe them.

Select two or three volunteers to describe the family influences that shaped their personalities. Do not allow these testimonies to become too personal or too negative. The point of this exercise is to acknowledge the powerful influence of our formative years.

The learning exercise on page 23 asks members to note their important life experiences at ages 12, 20, and 30. If time permits, have volunteers share some of their experiences.

Close with prayer, thanking God for making and shaping us through unique life experiences.

SESSION 3

Session Goals

To identify the first three characteristics of mental fitness: seeking godly wisdom, living as a thinking Christian, and continuing to learn and grow.

During the Session

Greet members and have them sign the attendance sheet. Call for prayer requests and enlist a volunteer to pray. Say or read together the Verse to Know (p. 25). Brainstorm possible meanings of having the "mind of Christ."

This week's study was introduced by a story of a student whose faith was challenged in college. Ask if anyone in the group has had a similar experience either at work or school. Invite him or her to share that experience.

Ask a volunteer to read Proverbs 9:10 (p. 26). Ask, *What does "the fear of the Lord" mean to you?* Ask members to share some practical ideas for pursuing wisdom and understanding that have been helpful for them.

Have members turn to the "Contrasts in Worldview" chart on page 29. Invite members to contrast secular and Christian solutions to problems that confront us today. Write these on a markerboard or posterboard.

Invite reactions to the statement on page 30: "The secular worldview is also a faith supposition."

Ask, Why do you think God had Moses and Daniel educated in all the learning of the cultures in which they lived? What value should a Christian place on education?

Invite responses to the learning activity on page 33. Emphasize the statement, "Humility is not low self-esteem" (p. 33). Say, *We are to thank God for our gifts, talents, and abilities.*

Review the **INREACH, OUTREACH, UPREACH**, and Professor Phitt suggestions in the margins.

As a group, complete the review exercise on page 34. Conclude the session by reading together the closing prayer on page 33.

SESSION 4

Session Goals

To identify three additional characteristics of mental fitness: have a healthy self-image, remember the importance of others, and maintain healthy boundaries with others.

During the Session

Greet members and have them sign the attendance sheet. Call for prayer requests and enlist a volunteer to pray. Say or read together the Verses to Know (p. 35). If someone has found it difficult to learn, point out key words and phrases. Repeat it several times together.

Ask someone to recall the story of Cindy and her difficulty changing her self-image (pp. 35-36). Ask members to name the three keys to a healthy self-image from page 37 as you write them on a markerboard or posterboard. Have members share areas of success and areas of difficulty with the three. Beside each key, write practical suggestions for growing in each area as members name them.

Invite responses to the statement (p. 38): "Authentic change is a gradual process, particularly when lifestyle habits are involved." Then ask members to share their responses to the UPREACH activity on page 38.

Encourage members to share their examples of humility from the learning exercise on page 38. Call attention to the outreach activity on page 38. Ask, *How would a person know if he or she is other-focused?*

Ask the group to agree or disagree with the priority list suggested by the author on page 39. Review the characteristics of a S.M.A.R.T. goal. Invite volunteers to share examples of their S.M.A.R.T. goals with the group.

Emphasize the importance of personal boundaries in relating to others. Discuss why boundaries are important and problems when boundaries aren't kept. Ask, *How do boundaries help you live a balanced life?*

Ask members to turn to the final learning activity on page 40. As a group, summarize each of the six characteristics. Close with prayer.

SESSION 5

Session Goals

To gain a better understanding of three obstacles to loving God with all our minds: the fall, temptations, and worldly influences.

During the Session

Greet members and have them sign the attendance sheet. Call for prayer requests and enlist a volunteer to pray. Say together the Verse to Know on page 41. Ask the group to give examples of the futility of thinking that is controlled by our fallen natures.

Have someone read Romans 7:15 (p. 41) and explain why Paul found it difficult to live in obedience to God. Emphasize Christ as the one who rescues us from eternal death and present struggles (Rom. 7:24).

Say or read together I Corinthians 10:13 on page 43. Ask for volunteers to give examples of the truth of this verse. Review ways God's promise helps us in the areas of nutrition and fitness. Point out that we must call on God for help in resisting temptation; His help is not automatic! From your Bible read Psalm 46:1 aloud.

Have a volunteer read Ephesians 6:10-18. Encourage volunteers to give examples of how each piece of armor can help in overcoming temptations we face in the areas of nutrition and exercise. Point out the benefits of using the *Accountability Journal* to track progress in these areas.

Ask members to give examples of the third obstacle, worldly influences. Write these on a markerboard or posterboard. Ask for responses to the OUTREACH activity on page 45.

Ask a volunteer to review the three keys to success in overcoming worldly influences (p. 46). From your Bibles read aloud 2 Timothy 2:22 as a group.

Read the quote by Charles Ryrie (p. 46). Call attention to the last learning exercise in week 5. Close with a prayer asking for God's help in setting personal limits, pursuing personal growth, and remaining accountable to spiritually healthy Christians.

SESSION 6

Session Goals

To understand how parental influence and past experiences may present obstacles to loving God with all our minds. To identify unrealistic assumptions that do not serve us well as rules by which to live our lives.

During the Session

Greet members and have them sign the attendance sheet. Call for prayer requests and enlist a volunteer to pray.

Ask members to recall the three results of unhealthy parenting Paul gave in Colossians 3:21 and Ephesians 6:4 (p. 48). Do not ask for personal responses to this learning activity, but ask volunteers to describe what a child and then an adult might look like who has become bitter, discouraged, or frustrated. Invite members to turn to the chart on page 50 for examples of how parenting styles can affect young children and produce future problems in adults.

A discussion like this will bring up painful memories in some members. Ask a volunteer to read Mark 10:13-16 (p. 51). Say or read together the prayer on page 51.

Emphasize that the unrealistic needs and expectations that parents have can lead to unrealistic thinking patterns in their children when they grow up. Ask members to locate the learning exercise at the top of page 52. Ask volunteers to give examples of actions and feelings that might result from some of these unrealistic assumptions.

As an optional activity, ask members to rephrase these assumptions into healthy assumptions, such as *Everything I do will not please others. I must learn to please God, not others, as my highest priority.*

Point out that this week's study is not meant to criticize our parents. Each of us must take responsibility for our thoughts, words, and actions. However, we must deal with the past in order for us to effectively put it behind us and move on to more realistic assumptions. Say Isaiah 43:18-19 together (p. 52). Close with prayer that God would show us the new things He is doing in our lives.

SESSION 7

Session Goals

To gain a better understanding of how God transforms our minds. To explain the four stages of the change process.

During the Session

Greet members and have them sign the attendance sheet. Call for prayer requests and enlist a volunteer to pray. Review the obstacles to loving God with all our minds found in Weeks 5 and 6.

Read Romans 12:1. Brainstorm what it means to offer our bodies as living sacrifices. Emphasize that this action is a response to the mercy God has shown us in Christ. Say together Romans 12:2, this week's Verse to Know. Ask, *How do we keep from being conformed to worldly standards? What results from a transformed mind?*

Have a volunteer read Romans 8:5-6. Ask, *What are the two choices that a person can make? What does it mean to have our minds controlled by God's Spirit?* Emphasize that the key to this week's study is that we can each choose to change and grow. God is the change agent.

Invite a volunteer to describe the three points emphasized by Paul in transforming a depraved mind into one that is controlled by God's Spirit (pp. 55-56). Point out that the result for us is the joy of living out God's will.

Invite a volunteer to share an experience similar to Brian and Gail's (pp. 53-54). Ask him or her to share what changed and what led to the change.

Review the change process by having members define and give an example of each of the four steps:
1. Develop Awareness
2. Grow in Knowledge
3. Take Action
4. Experience Change

(Optional) Ask volunteers to share their progress in reaching their goals for a renewed mind. Ask, What can we do to continue this change process? Close with prayer for each member's change process.

SESSION 8

Session Goals

To encourage personal change by learning to focus our attention upward to God. To learn the appropriate places to invest our thoughts.

During the Session

Greet members and have them sign the attendance sheet. Call for prayer requests and enlist a volunteer to pray.

Say, *This week you were asked to underline all the occurrences of the words* you *and* your *in Colossians 3:1-4 (p. 62).* As a group read the verses aloud inserting "my" or "I" in all the places where "you" and "your" occur. To encourage the group in this activity, you may want to read the passage first, inserting these changes.

Ask members to respond to the learning activity in the middle of page 62. Ask, *Why is it necessary to "die" to sin in order to live a new life?*

Write the following on a large sheet of paper or markerboard, or photocopy one for each member:

What God Has Done	**What This Means for Me Today**
Past	
Present	
Future	

Assign members to three groups (past, present, future) or complete the chart as a large group. After 2-3 minutes, reconvene the groups and ask a volunteer from each group to share the group report.

Read together Philippians 4:8-9. Review key ideas about each of the eight areas. Ask, *In the fishing story on pages 63-64, how did the father teach his son to focus on the truth?* Invite responses to the learning activity on page 66.

Review the unhealthy and healthy motivators for a transformed mind. Emphasize the importance of an action plan, such as the activity on page 68. Read Professor Phitt's advice on page 68. Close with prayer.

SESSION 9

Session Goals

To understand and befriend persons who face high hurdles. To identify high hurdles in our lives.

During the Session

Because of the sensitive nature of this week's material, do not allow group time to become a counseling session. Offer your assistance outside of class to pursue other avenues of help. If possible, display on a table at the front of the room some resources from your church media center that speak to these issues.

Greet members and have them sign the attendance sheet. Call for prayer requests and enlist a volunteer to pray. Say or read the Verse to Know.

Ask, *What are some of the thoughts and feelings that Paul experienced according to the verses on page 69?* Point out that this passage is a good example of how our thoughts and feelings are often closely connected and hard to separate.

Emphasize that God may want to use us to help someone who faces what the author calls high hurdles. Recall the importance of a "listening ear" from page 70. Discuss why listening is such an important gift to one who is hurting. Ask the question at the top of page 77.

Review the description of distorted thinking on page 74. Invite volunteers to share their responses to the learning activity that follows. Be prepared to share one of your own as a discussion starter.

Ask, *What keeps us in bondage to negative thought patterns? Why is repentance necessary to break the bondage?*

Assign members to groups of 2-4 people to discuss the two questions on page 77 (Spiritual Misconceptions). After 3-5 minutes, bring the groups together and have a volunteer from each group share what they concluded.

Read together 2 Corinthians 1:3-4. Review the three important lessons from this verse (p. 78). Close with prayer that God would use members of the group to share His comfort with others who are facing troubles.

SESSION 10

Session Goals

To review the major ideas from this study. To share progress on the mental wellness journey.

During the Session

This session serves as a review of the study and an opportunity for members to share progress on their wellness journey. Adapt the lesson plan to reflect the personality, needs, and interests of your group.

As the session begins, lead the group to recall answers to prayer during the past 10 weeks. Spend time praising God for His faithfulness. Say or read together the Verses to Know (p. 79). Ask, *What is the benefit of a steadfast mind?* (perfect peace). *How do we maintain a steadfast mind?* (trust).

Walk members through every page of this study, pausing to discuss ideas members have underlined or found especially helpful. This process may take more than half of the session. Here are some discussion starters:

1. How does the stress model (p. 12) help you analyze how you react to events/stressors?
2. What are the six characteristics of mental fitness that God invites us to enjoy? (p. 40)
3. What are the obstacles to loving God with all our minds? Encourage volunteers to share responses to the learning activity on page 82.
4. List the four steps in the change process (pp. 82-83).
5. How does God go about renewing our minds (pp. 82-83)? Invite volunteers to share to what extent these change processes are part of their lives.
6. What is a helpful process for changing distorted thinking? (p. 74) Invite volunteers to share their responses to the learning activity on page 84.

(Optional Plan) Use a game show format to review the six questions above, as well as additional questions you identified from your review.

Announce plans for next week's session. Encourage members to review the Verses to Know during the coming week. Close with prayer.

SESSION 11

Session Goals

To set goals to maintain progress in the mental wellness journey. To provide closure for the group experience.

During the Session

Select an option below or determine your own closure activities with the group. Additional options can be found in the lesson plans for the *Fit 4 Nutrition* and *Fit 4 Fitness* courses in the *Facilitator Guide* (see pp. 44 and 70).

Option 1:

Lead members to share what the group experience has meant to them. Provide materials such as construction paper, felt-tip markers, chenille craft stems, glue, and scissors. Instruct members to make a visual "thank you" for one or more members of the group. Make sure that no one is left out. Take turns making the presentations.

Select volunteers to review the obstacles they face and the plans they are following to love God with all of their minds. Pray for each person who shares.

Review the study's Verses to Know. Encourage members to continue using the *Accountability Journal* (ordering information on p. 95). Announce plans for the next *Fit 4* continuing study or other discipleship option. Close with prayer and a word of encouragement.

Option 2:

Consider a story that highlights the growth of an individual toward mental wellness as defined in this study. The story could be a Bible story, a familiar novel, a children's book, or an appropriate movie. If you choose the movie, allow time to view the movie and discuss it. You may want to host this meeting in a home. Plan accordingly.

Use comments and questions such as: Describe how the main character(s) grew in their relationship with God, self, and others. What can we learn from their journey toward mental wellness? What obstacles were they required to face and overcome? How would you respond if facing the same difficulties?

Lead the class in a time of commitment to continued mental wellness and close with a thanksgiving prayer.

FIT 4 RESOURCES

Fit 4 *Plan Kit*

Includes two copies of the *Facilitator Guide,* four group session videotapes, promotional/facilitator training video, *Nutrition Starter Kit,* and *Fitness Starter Kit.* 0-6330-0580-0

Fit 4 *Nutrition Starter Kit*

This 12-week course includes a *Nutrition Member Workbook, Accountability Journal Refill Pack* and three-ring binder, *Wise Choices Fit 4 Cookbook,* and lunch bag imprinted with *Fit 4* logo. 0-6330-0581-9

Fit 4 Nutrition Member Workbook 0-6330-2883-5

Fit 4 *Fitness Starter Kit*

A 12-week course that includes a *Fitness Member Workbook, Accountability Journal Refill Pack* and three-ring binder, the *Fit 4 Workout* video, and exercise bag imprinted with *Fit 4* logo. 0-6330-0582-7

Fit 4 Fitness Member Workbook 0-6330-2010-9

Fit 4 *Facilitator Guide*

Contains group session plans for facilitating both basic courses. Two copies included in *Plan Kit.* 0-6330-0588-6

Fit 4 *Accountability Journal Refill Pack*

Space to record meals and exercise activities for 13 weeks. Includes helpful nutritional and fitness information. 0-6330-0589-4

Wise Choices **Fit 4** *Cookbook*

Contains easy-to-prepare recipes, menu planning suggestions, a grocery shopping list, food terms, label-reading instructions, and snack suggestions. 0-6330-0587-8

Fit 4 *Continuing Studies*

- *With All My Heart: God's Design for Emotional Wellness* 0-6330-0583-5
- *With All My Soul: God's Design for Spiritual Wellness* 0-6330-0585-1
- *With All My Mind: God's Design for Mental Wellness* 0-6330-0584-3
- *With All My Strength: God's Design for Physical Wellness* 0-6330-0586-X, (available December 2002)

Fit4.com *Web Site*

Up-to-date nutritional and fitness information, calculators for health assessments, fun quizzes, recipes, and more. Features on all four areas of wellness.

Christian Health Magazine

Provides current health information, articles about people on wellness journeys, helpful tips, recipes, and spiritual truths to keep our lives focused on Christ. It's a great outreach tool for your church; place copies in medical offices and other businesses.

fit 4
heart • soul • mind • strength
A LIFEWAY CHRISTIAN WELLNESS PLAN

TO ORDER COPIES OF THESE RESOURCES:

Write LifeWay Church Resources Customer Service; One LifeWay Plaza; Nashville, TN 37234-0113; Fax order to (615) 251-5933; Phone 1-800-458-2772; Email to *customerservice@lifeway.com;* Order online at *www.lifeway.com;* or visit the LifeWay Christian Store serving you.

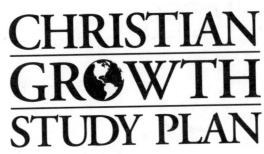

CHRISTIAN GROWTH STUDY PLAN

Preparing Christians to Serve

In the **Christian Growth Study Plan (formerly Church Study Course),** this book *With All My Mind* is a resource for course credit in the subject area Personal Life of the Christian Growth category of diploma plans. To receive credit, read the book, complete the learning activities, show your work to your pastor, a staff member or church leader, then complete the following information. This page may be duplicated. Send the completed page to:

**Christian Growth Study Plan
One LifeWay Plaza
Nashville, TN 37234-0117
FAX: (615)251-5067**

For information about the Christian Growth Study Plan, refer to the current Christian Growth Study Plan Catalog. Your church office may have a copy. If not, request a free copy from the Christian Growth Study Plan office (615/251-2525).

With All My Mind
COURSE NUMBER: CG-0536

PARTICIPANT INFORMATION

Social Security Number (USA ONLY-optional)	Personal CGSP Number*	Date of Birth (MONTH, DAY, YEAR)

Name (First, Middle, Last)	Home Phone

Address (Street, Route, or P.O. Box)	City, State, or Province	Zip/Postal Code

CHURCH INFORMATION

Church Name

Address (Street, Route, or P.O. Box)	City, State, or Province	Zip/Postal Code

CHANGE REQUEST ONLY

☐ Former Name		
☐ Former Address	City, State, or Province	Zip/Postal Code
☐ Former Church	City, State, or Province	Zip/Postal Code

Signature of Pastor, Conference Leader, or Other Church Leader	Date

*New participants are requested but not required to give SS# and date of birth. Existing participants, please give CGSP# when using SS# for the first time. Thereafter, only one ID# is required. **Mail to:** Christian Growth Study Plan, One LifeWay Plaza, Nashville, TN 37234-0117. Fax: (615)251-5067.

Rev. 10-01